Maggie Black has written on international issues,
including for UNICEF, WaterAid and the
Global Water Partnership. Her books include: *Water Life Force,*
NoNonsense Guides on *Water* and *International Development,*
Water: A Matter of Life and Health (with Rupert Talbot),
and *The Last Taboo: Opening the Door on
the Global Sanitation Crisis* (with Ben Fawcett).

Atlases by New Internationalist

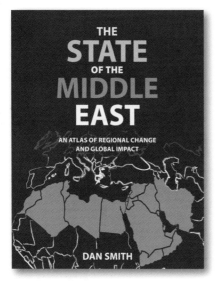

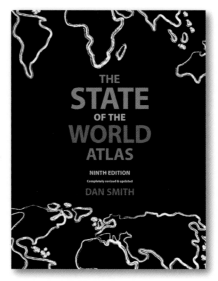

ISBN: 978-1-78026-231-4 |
Paperback | £14.99

ISBN: 978-1-78026-121-8 |
Paperback | £14.99

New Internationalist m̃ www.myriadeditions.com

New Internationalist m̃ www.myriadeditions.com

'A brilliant, accessible up-to-date
resource: everything you need to
know to fuel your understanding of
this complex region.'

— Jon Snow

'No-one wishing to keep a grip on the
reality of the world should be without
these books.'

— *International Herald Tribune*

THE
STATE
OF THE
WORLD'S
WATER

An Atlas of Our Most Vital Resource

MAGGIE BLACK

New Internationalist

newint.org

This third edition first published
by New Internationalist in 2016

New Internationalist
The Old Music Hall, 106-108 Cowley Road, Oxford OX4 1JE
newint.org

Myriad Editions
59 Lansdowne Place, Brighton BN3 1FL
www.myriadeditions.com

1 3 5 7 9 10 8 6 4 2

The moral right of the author has been asserted.

ISBN: 978-1-78026-373-1
ISBN ebook: 978-1-78026-375-5

Edited and coordinated by Jannet King
Design, maps and graphics by Isabelle Lewis

Printed on paper produced from sustainable sources.
Printed and bound in Hong Kong through Lion Production
under the supervision of Bob Cassels, The Hanway Press, London.

A CIP catalogue record for this book is available from the
British Library.

CONTENTS

Introduction   9
Acknowledgements   15
Useful Conversions   16
Glossary   17

PART 1 A FINITE RESOURCE   18

1 GLOBAL WATER   20
The volume of water in the world never changes, but only 2.5% is fresh, and more than two-thirds of this is unavailable for human use.

2 WATER'S UNEQUAL DISTRIBUTION   22
The amount of water that falls as rain, filling lakes, rivers, streams and aquifers, remains constant. At present we are still using less than a third.

3 WATER SHORTAGE   24
The spectre of water shortage is less a global phenomenon than one threatening particular regions and localities.

4 RISING DEMAND   26
Around 4,000 cubic kilometres of fresh water are withdrawn every year – equivalent to roughly 1,700 litres per person per day.

5 DWINDLING SUPPLY   28
About a fifth of water used comes from aquifers. Some are replenished, but many are non-renewable and are being irreversibly mined.

6 COMPETITION AND CONFLICT   30
As populations grow, and more water is extracted per person, there is increasing competition and conflict over the exploitation of river waters and aquifers.

7 ENVIRONMENTAL SECURITY   32
Aquatic ecosystems make a vital contribution to environmental security.

PART 2 WATER AND CLIMATE CHANGE   34

8 ICE AND SNOW MELT   36
Climate change is likely to affect river flow in many complex ways.

9 STORMS AND FLOODS   38
Life-threatening and destructive floods are becoming more frequent and affecting an increasing number of people.

10 DROUGHTS   40
The world's drylands will become drier as a result of climate change.

11 RIVER BASIN STRESSES   42
Seasonal changes in river flow and temperature of fresh water affect water quality.

PART 3 WATER FOR LIVING   44

12 WATER FOR DRINKING   46
Everyone has access to a source of drinking water but in an increasingly crowded world most natural sources are contaminated.

13 WATER FOR FOOD   48
All food production depends on water, so water stress leads to stress on the global and family food basket.

14 WATER FOR SANITATION   50
Many lower-cost sanitation systems in the developing world use no water or very little.

15 WATER IN THE CITY   52
The increasing number of people living in towns and cities is exerting huge pressure on municipal infrastructure and services.

16 WATER AT HOME   54
There are huge discrepancies in the amount of water people use in their home, depending on lifestyle and availability.

17 WATER AND DISEASE   56
Water's critical role in hygiene and sanitation, and in the spread of diarrhoeal disease, confers on it a central place in public health.

PART 4 WATER FOR ECONOMIC PRODUCTION   58

18 WATER FOOTPRINT   60
Industrialized lifestyles involve the consumption of large amounts of "virtual" water embedded in foodstuffs and in manufactured items.

19 WATER FOR IRRIGATION   62
Around two-thirds of water withdrawals are for irrigation, which supports a fifth of the world's cropland.

20 WATER FOR FISHERIES   64
Fish make a major contribution to the global food supply and are increasingly farmed as a cash crop.

21 WATER FOR INDUSTRY   66
Just over 20 per cent of all freshwater withdrawals are for industry.

22 WATER FOR ENERGY   68
Water plays a vital role in the generation of electricity.

23 TRANSPORT AND LEISURE   70
Water is integral to many productive and cultural activities not easily traceable in economic statistics.

24 WATER FOR SALE   72
The sale of water is an inevitable part of any organized delivery system, but in general the wealthy pay less than the poor.

Part 5 Damaged Water 74

25 Dammed Rivers 76
Nearly 60 per cent of major rivers are impeded by large dams.

26 Dispossession by Water 78
Rivers need to be managed so as to sustain the lives of those dependent on them.

27 Water Pollutants 80
Globally, 2 million tons of sewage, industrial and agricultural waste are discharged into the world's waterways every year.

28 Water Pollution 82
Rapid urbanization and accelerating industrialization are causing increased water pollution and corresponding environmental threats.

29 Damaged Waterways 84
Industrialization is damaging the world's waterways.

30 Threatened Ecologies 86
Even subtle changes in quality, temperature or seasonal availability of fresh water can have a devastating effect on the living organisms that inhabit it.

Part 6 Water for the Future 88

31 Technological Fixes 90
Technological innovations and adaptations have a role in meeting the mounting threats to freshwater supplies.

32 The Rising Price of Water 92
Water is a vital resource to which everyone has a right, but it is also seen as a commodity for which a realistic price should be paid.

33 Treaties and Obligations 94
More than 260 river basins are shared between countries, and equitable use of their waters requires negotiation and agreement.

34 Striving for Co-operation 96
The spectre of growing competition between states over water has generated fighting talk, especially in retaliation against upstream behaviour.

35 Managing the Future 98
The real world water crisis is a crisis of water management.

Part 7 Data Tables and Sources 100

Needs and Resources 102
Water Uses 110
Sources 118
Index 125

INTRODUCTION

Water means life – a truism so often repeated that its significance becomes lost. This vital natural resource – falling from the sky, bubbling up into springs and lakes, flowing in streams and rivers – is so fundamental to human activity that everyone must have access to it. Leaving aside questions of unequal power over resources, the very nature of water militates against this. Rain may fall equally "on the just and on the unjust fellow", but everything depends on where they are standing. There is nothing "just" about annual rainfall distribution, which varies from a few millimetres in some places to thousands in others. And as the climate comes under increasing pressure, the meteorological patterns that scientists have worked for generations to understand are becoming even less predictable. Rainfall, which regenerates all other surface and underground sources, may be about to become even more unjust than before.

Rain's erratic choice of landing place, from deserts to forests, tropical to temperate zones, mountains to valleys, is not the end of this complicated story. Unlike other elements on which life depends, it frequently changes its state – from liquid to vapour, from liquid to ice, and *vice versa*, depending on the season. Water in lakes and reservoirs is constantly evaporating. And water in the landscape never stands still – it is always on the move. It seeps into the soil for use by plants and creatures, or percolates into aquifers where it renews underground supplies. It travels downhill on even the slightest of gradients. Navigating around whatever impediments it finds in its way, surface water enters a complex system of streams and tributaries, joining an ever larger flow destined for the sea. Many of these linked river networks are occupied by different peoples, states and jurisdictions.

At any and every stage along its journey, water is used – and sometimes re-used several times – to support life and economic activity. Maximizing its potential for different uses and environments requires technology, investment, control of pollution, regulation, and efficient service delivery. Take just one example. Rain falling on the Tibetan Plateau finds its way into China's Lancang river. At many stages downstream, flow is diverted by hydraulic construction and human ingenuity into paddy fields to grow rice. Elsewhere, the speeding stream generates electricity when channelled through hydropower turbines. Towns and cities remove water for human consumption and industry, and discharge wastewater back into it. As the river slows and broadens in its lower reaches, becoming the Mekong, it supports a vast aquatic environment on which local fisherman and wildlife depend. Eventually, it enters the South China Sea, having passed through six countries and been endlessly manipulated and exploited along the way.

Heightened demand

In an ever more crowded world, the processes involved in this manipulation and exploitation – repeated in countless river basins large and small – are becoming increasingly complex. Much more is being demanded of hard-pressed resources. Rivers are increasingly fragmented by dams. Upstream users reduce both the volume and the quality of water descending downstream. Non-renewable supplies, in the form of fossil-water aquifers formed millennia ago, are becoming rapidly exhausted. Every drop of available supply has to be harnessed to agricultural, industrial or domestic use – and sometimes all three in sequence. The volume of renewable supplies remains constant and is unlikely to falter, despite the many meteorological fluctuations associated with global warming. But the pressures exerted on this finite supply, both from increased population, and from the increasing number of people expecting to enjoy an industrialized lifestyle, are profound. Competition between different types of use, and between upstream and downstream users, is becoming more acute. The extraordinary nature of the substance compounds the many difficulties of managing water in such a way that all these conflicting interests are adjudicated fairly.

Awareness of the critical limits on freshwater supplies has been growing over the past 20 years, alongside more profound appreciation of environmental constraints. Indeed, the circulation of water in the environment – to preserve wetlands, conserve biodiversity, and protect climate stability – has itself become recognized as a category of "water use" necessary to nurture the planet and its other life-giving resources. One strategy for water conservation has been to attach an economic value to all its uses and apply market instruments, such as water-pricing, to prevent profligate extraction and consumption. But the treatment of water as a commodity like any other, to be traded and used for corporate profit-making, has caused huge resentment. In those societies where poverty is acute, and rural farmers and urban dwellers are surviving at levels close to subsistence, unsubsidized water services effectively mean no water services at all. However important it is to conserve supplies, the story of water will be even more unjust if the least well-off bear a disproportionate burden of the costs.

In fact, the problem of water as it relates to people in non-industrial environments is that most of them use too little water, rather than too much. Around 700 million people are still without a reliable source of drinking water, and 2.4 billion people are without basic sanitation. Having no tap at home constrains water use to the point where lack of personal hygiene is at least as much of a disease risk as lack of safe drinking water. Any attempt to improve water management in such a way as to make distribution more just should spread services to those with no protected water supply, many of whom currently spend much more on water purchased by the litre and carried home in a pot, than those living where pipes and taps are prolific.

With water, as with pressure on other natural resources, it is not the poor who are pumping up industrial-scale quantities to sell as a marketized commodity, or to irrigate sugar or cotton plantations in unsuitable dryland environments. Nor are they manufacturing or buying televisions, computers, cars or other sophisticated consumer products. It is not the disadvantaged and underfed who are polluting rivers with pesticide residues and chemical wastes, or eating farmed fish or hamburgers requiring large quantities of water for their production. The industrial lifestyle is propped up by water even more than it is propped up by oil.

Water profligacy

Food is one of the most thirsty water consumers. Over 70 percent of water withdrawals are used for agriculture, to irrigate fields or spray crops. But much of this water fails to reach its target – the roots of the plants; it is lost to the atmosphere, or returned to the water system unused. If poorly managed, channel irrigation can actually damage the soil, leaving it saline and unproductive. For this and many other reasons, including the social disruption and environmental damage caused by large dams, it is generally acknowledged that the train of "progress", in which large-scale irrigation projects opened up new agricultural land for cultivation, has run into the buffers.

Despite the uneven distribution of land ownership and cheap food, since the expansion of food production that accompanied the Green Revolution it has been possible to envisage a time when no child would go to bed hungry. But over 780 million people are still without a sufficient or nutritious diet, and making a serious dent in the hunger figures is becoming increasingly difficult. If food production is to keep pace with increasing population, and prices are to be kept in check, water efficiency in agriculture will have to be given far more attention. Volumes available for agriculture are likely to decline or remain static as industry and expanding urban centres increase their share.

Technology will have to be harnessed to reducing water wastefulness. Up to now, hybrid seeds have mostly required extra water for cultivation; more attention will have to be focused on plant strains that require less water. Farmers will have to rediscover respect for environmental parameters, with drylands used for drought-resistant grains and tubers. Investment is needed in small-scale irrigation and water-harvesting techniques, which could improve the livelihoods of millions of farming families, especially in Africa but also in South Asia. Irrigation needs to be carefully managed, and combined with measures to improve the water-holding quality of the soil, nurture its fertility and increase yields from rain-fed crops. As pressures mount, food production will have to focus on items that use less water per unit of energy or nutrition than the red meat so highly prized in Western cultures.

Reduction of water profligacy and improved efficiency are also needed for water use in manufacturing. In many Western countries, water conservation has been enforced by regulation and pricing to the point that recent expansion in industrial water use has been relatively constrained. The challenge is to ensure that these kinds of measures are taken up by less developed and industrializing countries, where water governance and regulatory frameworks are weaker and more frequently flouted. On the domestic front, appliances such as toilets and washing-machines that use less water are now widely available, but even these, as they are taken up by the new middle-class in countries such as China and India, will have a major impact on the quantity of fresh water used in towns and cities, and on the quantity of wastewater discarded.

The amount of water used per household varies enormously around the world, and a large part of it is invisible. Consumption is not limited to drinking, bathing, flushing the toilet, using the dishwasher and watering the garden, adding up to well over 100 litres per capita a day. Everything that is manufactured – from electronic equipment to newspapers and kitchen gadgets – has involved water in its production. The total amount of water each person consumes if such products are factored into our "water footprint" is far higher than the figure for direct consumption. Nor is usage restricted to water from local sources: it also includes water embedded in food and goods imported from elsewhere. Thus water-stressed areas in Africa, America, Asia and Australia may be used to produce consumer items for export, while – with real injustice – local farmers and herders go short.

Pollution

At the same time as demand on volumes increase, pressures mount on freshwater quality. No longer can natural water from springs, dug wells and running rivers automatically be assumed to be clean and safe to drink. The natural capacity of waterways to act as the world's inbuilt dish-washing apparatus is inadequate to cope with the overload of wastes from increased population density. Many towns and cities in the developing world suffer the indignity of London 150 years ago when, in a hot summer season, the Thames was reduced to a Great Stink by a combination of upstream take-off and raw sewage inflows. Around 90 percent of human waste in the developing world is still discharged untreated into rivers. Since the threat of a cholera epidemic by the intake of foul air no longer causes the alarm it once did, the public-health incentive for dealing with this nuisance is not what it used to be.

An overload of human waste in rivers, lakes and streams destroys plant and aquatic life and can carry with it bacteria and viruses that cause serious diseases. The pollution caused by chemical wastes and industrial spills may not be as visible, but may be even more damaging. Where pesticide residues and pharmaceutical ingredients are washed into rivers or leached into the soil and from there enter the food chain, their toxic effects may build up in human tissues and cause long-term ill-health. Some pollutants may be traced thousands of miles from where they were originally discharged. For too long, the world's freshwater and seawater network has been considered as having an unlimited capacity to function as humanity's sink. As a result, many parts of the network have become degraded.

Co-operation over water

The increasing pressure on water resources has led to intense competition. Within one community, it is often hard to agree who has the right to take freely from the source for irrigation purposes, or whether people with a tap in their yard should pay a higher rate than those still obliged to walk to the pump. Should fines be imposed on people whose tannery, or cloth-dying business, or latrine has fouled the local source? These are questions that have exercised communities for centuries. At the local level, water governance has always demanded co-operation, often reinforced by water's venerated place in human affairs. But as lifestyles become more water-intensive, and the supply is tampered with at ever greater distances, these problems become more acute, especially at the wider level of district or nation, up to multinational level.

Many fear that water is becoming a commercialized commodity, with market forces left to decide who gets to use it or abuse it. Fortunately, that prospect is retreating. Irresponsible profit-making and corruption over water services – the result of inflated expectations from the privatization of services and the efficacy of markets – and the difficulties entailed in persuading customers and authorities to accept much higher pricing regimes, has induced a major re-think about optimal systems of water distribution and its management between public and private sectors. Compared to 10 or 20 years ago, there is now a much wider appreciation that water is a common good, and that it ought to be managed in the common interest by authorities that are answerable in the public domain, even though the role of the private sector has become more ubiquitous. When the task of reconciling all the different user interests is understood in all its parameters, the likelihood is that the business of "water diplomacy" among public and private practitioners will continue to be a growth industry in the 21st century.

The idea of "integrated water resources management" sounds so reasonable and just – reconciling upstream and downstream users, allocating so much to agriculture and so much to industry, bringing in all parties across all political boundaries to the river basin forum – that it ought to be adopted universally and without delay. But its realization requires a complex process of reconciling competing claims, and a willingness to share a natural resource in an equitable way; therefore, such an achievement would be virtually unprecedented in human history. The omens, however, are more positive than might be thought. Despite all the talk about "water wars", experience shows that co-operation over water has occurred more often than conflict, and that antagonists with deeply held differences in almost every sphere can manage to find common cause over water. In the end, the unjust distribution of water in the landscape may provide the stimulus for humanity to find a way of sharing this life-giving resource, and thereby further the cause of bringing humanity together to seek ways of living in peace on our much-pressurized planet.

Maggie Black
Oxford
February 2016

ACKNOWLEDGEMENTS

The authors and publishers gratefully acknowledge the help generously given in the form of maps and data by the following individuals and institutions:

The WHYMAP team, Bundesanstalt für Geowissenschaften und Rohstoffe (BGR), for use of the groundwater resources map on pages 28–29; Center for Environmental Systems Research, University of Kassel for the map of environmental stress due to flow alteration on pages 76–77; Aaron Wolf and Lucia DeStefano of the Program in Water Conflict Management and Transformation, Oregon State University for data used on pages 94–97.

We would also like to thank the following photographers and organizations who have supplied images:

18 Silvrshootr / iStock; **22** NASA; **23** CGIAR; **30** Brendan Mulligan / IWLP; **31** NortyNort /CC License; **32** Davor Lavincic / iStock; Steve Garvie / CC License; Dmitry A Mottl / CC License; **34** cdrin / Shutterstock; **37** Monteratsch Glacier www.swisseduc.ch; **38** NOAA Climate Prediction; **44** ranplett/iStock; **50** www.groundwork.org; **53** CONAGUA - Organismo de Cuenca Aguas del Valle de México; **54** UNICEF Zambia; **57** WHO; World Bank / Eric Miller; **58** Bjoern Wylezich/ Shutterstock; **63** USDA; **64** Clement Tardif / Greenpeace; Don Hinrichsen; **66** Esperanza; **70** Great Lakes: The Soo Locks between Lake Superior and the St Marys River / US Army Corps of Engineers employee; Amazon cruise: www.travelwizard; **71** Canal boat: Graham Heywood / iStockphoto; Artificial beach, Paris: www.aquamedia; Kerala: Robert Churchill / iStockphoto; Golf course: Sheldon Kralstein; **74** wonderisland/Shutterstock; **76** GHG emissions: International Rivers; Colorado: Mark Byzewski / CC License; Patagonia: Gary Hughes / International Rivers; Australia: Hullwarren / CC License; **79** International Rivers; **82** San Joaquin: Alison M. Jones / www.nowater-nolife.org; Gulf of Mexico: NOAA; **83** Baltic Sea: http://earthobservatory.nasa.gov; India: Ryan ruffin_ready / CC License; **84** Agencia Brasil; **85** Dead fish: Alan Septoff / Tibor Kocsis media. earthworksaction.org; Chinese protestors: www.pacificenvironment.org; **87** Flamingos: Charles Schug / iStockphoto; Otters: John Stezler / iStockphoto; Frog: Samuli Siltanen / iStockphoto; Crocodile: Keiichi Hiki / iStockphoto; Trout: Laurin Johnson / iStockphoto; Crayfish: Stephen Moore / Dept of Conservation, New Zealand; **88** Desalination plant: James Grellier / CC License; **91** Seawater greenhouse: courtesy Charlie Paton, Seawater Greenhouse Ltd ; Fluoride filter: India Natural Resources Economics and Management (INREM) Foundation; **93** Right2Water; www. worldforum.org; **94** World Bank flickr library; **96** US Geological Survey; **97** Prill Mediendesign & Fotografie/iStockphoto; **98** Armenia: Global Environment Facility Small Grant's Facility; Cameroon: Global Water Partnership; **99** Marco Betti / Water Aid; **100** Peter Jeffreys/Shutterstock

Glossary

aquifer – a natural underground layer, often of sand or gravel, that contains water; some aquifers are very deep and in hard rock, and have taken millions of years to accumulate their supply.

billion – a thousand million.

blue water – water withdrawn from lakes, rivers and aquifers for irrigation.

brackish water – water that is neither **fresh** nor **salt**.

consumptive use – water that is used in, for example, manufacturing, agriculture and food, which is not therefore returned to a water resource. It excludes evaporation, which eventually returns to earth as rain.

desalination – the changing of **salt** or **brackish** water into **fresh** water; *see also* **reverse osmosis**.

evaporation – the process of liquid water becoming water vapour, including vaporization from water surfaces, land surfaces, and snow fields, but not from leaf surfaces.

evapotranspiration – both **evaporation** and **transpiration** (the process by which water is evaporated from a plant surface, such as leaf pores).

fresh water – water that contains fewer than 1,000 milligrams per litre of dissolved solids.

green water – rain water, in the context of agriculture

groundwater – water that lies deep underground in aquifers. Normally free of contamination, it is regarded as a safe source of drinking water.

impoundment – control of water by dam or embankment to prevent water from flowing along its natural course.

improved sanitation – toilet facilities that hygienically separate human excreta from human contact. These include "wet" systems, where water in a U-shaped pipe creates a seal, and which may be connected to a sewer or septic tank, and "dry" systems such as a pit toilet with a cleanable squat plate, cover and solidly constructed pit. Sanitation is considered adequate if it can effectively prevent human, animal and insect contact with faeces; this excludes public toilets in most settings.

improved water source – a water source with protection from contamination, such as a household connection to a safe piped supply or a public standpipe similarly connected; a borehole or protected well; a covered spring or rainwater collection system.

internal renewable water resources – average annual flow of rivers and recharge of groundwater generated from **precipitation** falling within the country's borders.

leaching – the process by which soluble materials in the soil, such as salts, nutrients, pesticide chemicals or contaminants, are washed into a lower layer of soil, or are dissolved and carried away by water.

melt-water – water produced by the melting of snow or ice.

precipitation – rain, snow, hail, sleet, dew, and frost.

renewable resources – total resources offered by the average annual natural inflow and run-off that feed a catchment area or aquifer; natural resources that, after exploitation, can return to their previous stock levels by the natural processes of growth or replenishment.

reverse osmosis – a desalination process that uses a semi-permeable membrane to separate and remove dissolved solids, viruses, bacteria and other matter from water; **salt** or **brackish** water is forced across a membrane, leaving the impurities behind and creating **fresh water**.

river basin – the area of land drained by a river and its tributaries. A basin is considered "closed" when its water is over-committed to human uses, and "closing" when it is approaching that state.

run-off – the movement of rain water over ground.

salt water – water that contains significant amounts of dissolved solids.

sewerage – a system of pipes with household connections to larger receptor and interceptor pipes and tunnels, that carries off waste matter, either to a treatment plant or directly to a river or stream.

surface water – water pumped from sources open to the atmosphere, such as rivers, lakes, and reservoirs.

unimproved water source – vendor, tanker trucks, and unprotected wells and springs.

wastewater treatment – the process of turning contaminated water into water that can be re-used for a range of purposes, depending on the level to which it has been treated.

water table – the upper level of groundwater in soil.

withdrawal – water removed from groundwater or surface water for use.

USEFUL CONVERSIONS

1 cubic metre (m^3) = 1,000 litres

1 cubic kilometre (km^3) = 1,000,000,000 cubic metres (m^3) = 1,000,000,000,000 litres

1 litre = 0.264 US gallons (liquid) = 0.219 UK gallons

1 US gallon (liquid) = 3.785 litres

1 UK gallon = 4.55 litres

1 cubic metre (m^3) = 264.172 US gallons (liquid) = 219.9 UK gallons

1 US gallon (liquid) = 0.00378 cubic metres = 3,785 cubic centimetres (cc)

1 UK gallon = 0.00454 cubic metres = 4,546 cubic centimetres (cc)

1 cubic kilometre (km^3) = 810,713 acre feet

1 acre foot = 1,233 cubic metres (m^3) = 325,851 US gallons (liquid)

1 kilometre (km) = 0.621 miles

1 mile = 1.6 kilometres (km)

1 kilogram (kg) = 2.2 pounds (lb)

1 pound (lb) = 0.45 kilograms (kg) = 450 grams (g)

Metric water–weight conversion

1 kilogram (kg) of water = 1 litre of water

1 gram of water = 1 cubic centimetre (cc) of water

1 metric tonne (mt) of water = 1,000 kilogram (kg) of water = 1,000 litres of water = 1 cubic metre (m^3)

PART 1 A Finite Resource

Water, fundamental to all life and human activity, is under serious threat. This is not because the supply is dwindling significantly – although some aquifers containing irreplaceable fossil water are being exhausted. The renewable supply of water on which planetary survival and well-being depend remains constant. Moisture evaporated by the sun from seas, soil and vegetation is released as rain to nourish plant growth and fill rivers, lakes and underground aquifers. Climate change may be influencing the localized behaviour and impacts of this "hydrological cycle", but this is not the most immediate threat.

Water falls unevenly in different latitudes and terrains, but there ought to be enough to meet humanity's needs. The problem lies in the way its consumption per head has been rising much faster than population growth. An increasing number of people with industrialized lifestyles consume diets rich in foodstuffs needing extra water to produce, and demand goods such as cars, television sets and computers whose manufacture also requires large volumes of water. This places excessive demands on vulnerable sources, stretching the available supply to its physical limits – especially in less well-endowed regions such as the Middle East.

The ability to control water and manage its use for productive purposes has always been central to human and economic development. Leaders of the ancient world depended on hydraulic works – dams, lifting devices and artificial lakes – to develop and maintain their civilizations. They fully understood the variability of rainfall and run-off that constituted the universal freshwater problem, long before today's pressures had to be taken into account.

Those living in water-short areas or those with seasonal rains tackle their problems by capturing run-off behind dams, and storing or diverting water for agricultural or other uses. As more water is manipulated in this way, the environmental and other limits of this approach have become apparent. Upstream and downstream users of the same resource, in river basins and watersheds, are forced into dispute as populations grow and demands increase.

However unevenly distributed, the supplies provided by natural forces are going to have to suffice. New ways of managing water will have to be found in order to maintain quantity and quality and achieve a fair distribution of a substance essential to life on Earth.

1 GLOBAL WATER

The volume of water in the world never changes, but only 2.5 per cent is fresh. More than two-thirds of fresh water is locked up in polar ice-caps and permanent snow cover. Of the rest, a small proportion is in lakes and streams, and the rest in underground aquifers.

Working in tandem, salt and fresh waters power life on Earth by a dynamic and constantly regenerative process. The sun's heat evaporates water from seas and lakes, and moisture in vegetation is absorbed into the air through evapotranspiration.

Once in the atmosphere, water vapour condenses into droplets. Clouds form from which rain and snow are released. This replenishes rivers and aquifers, enabling them to nourish soil fertility and promote plant growth.

The "hydrological cycle" depicts the forces energizing and controlling the movement of water from land, to sea, sky, and back to land. This 20th-century gem of hydrological analysis has had an important influence on ideas of a "global water supply" to be shared among humankind, and the pressures on that supply that today constitute a "global water crisis".

However, it is at the local level – arid, temperate, tropical, mountainous, riverine – that humanity interacts with water, storing, conserving, managing and distributing it. This is also where the impacts of climate change – rising sea levels, changed rainfall patterns – are felt. "Global water", for all practical purposes, is simply a useful construct.

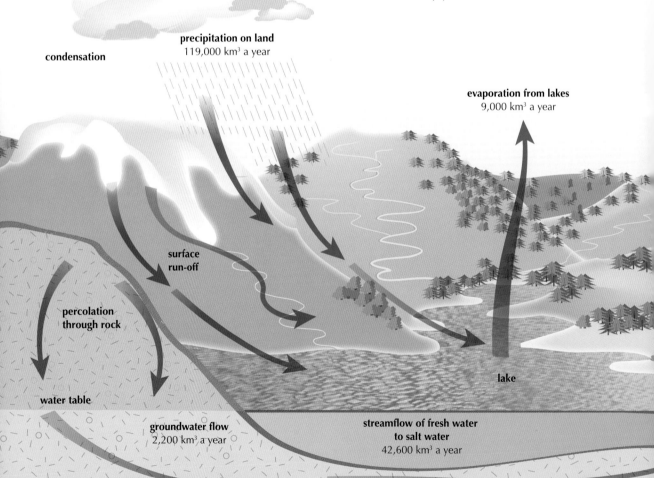

condensation

precipitation on land
119,000 km³ a year

evaporation from lakes
9,000 km³ a year

surface run-off

percolation through rock

lake

water table

groundwater flow
2,200 km³ a year

streamflow of fresh water to salt water
42,600 km³ a year

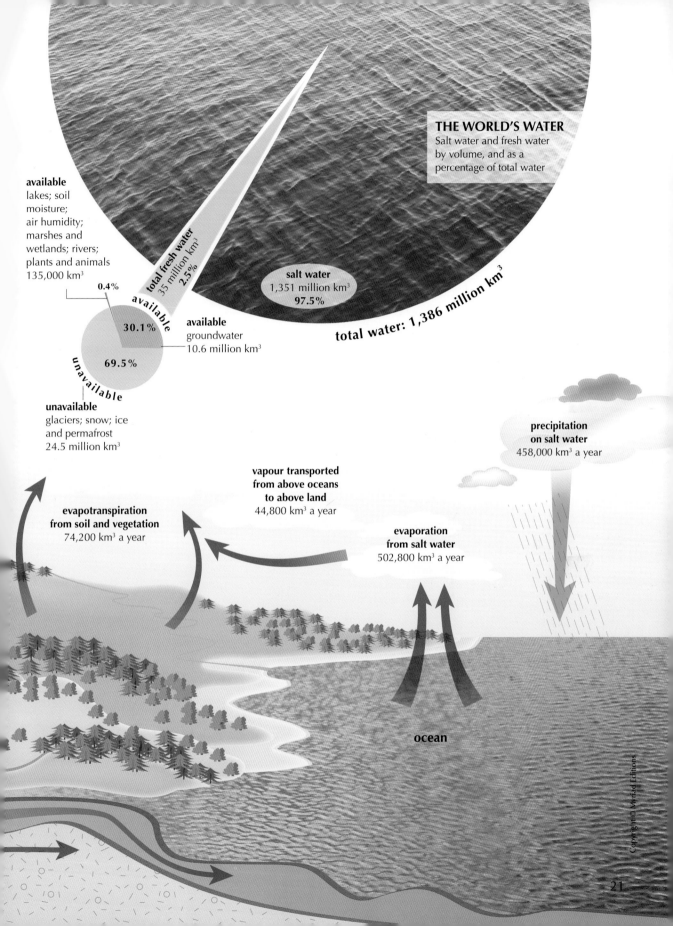

THE WORLD'S WATER
Salt water and fresh water by volume, and as a percentage of total water

available
lakes; soil moisture; air humidity; marshes and wetlands; rivers; plants and animals 135,000 km³

total fresh water 35 million km³ **2.5%**

salt water 1,351 million km³ **97.5%**

0.4%

available 30.1%

available groundwater 10.6 million km³

69.5%

unavailable

unavailable glaciers; snow; ice and permafrost 24.5 million km³

total water: 1,386 million km³

precipitation on salt water 458,000 km³ a year

vapour transported from above oceans to above land 44,800 km³ a year

evapotranspiration from soil and vegetation 74,200 km³ a year

evaporation from salt water 502,800 km³ a year

ocean

2 WATER'S UNEQUAL DISTRIBUTION

1.2 billion
people live in areas where little water falls or flows

The amount of water that falls as rain, filling lakes, rivers, streams and aquifers, is more than enough to meet our needs, but it is unevenly distributed across the Earth.

The floodplains of major rivers have water in abundance, and the need to control and deploy water within them helped prompt the birth of civilizations. In arid zones, tropical and frozen, lack of water constrains human settlement and very different societies have emerged.

In temperate areas with steady and reliable rainfall, much of which soaks into the ground, it has been relatively easy to manage freshwater flows so as to secure supplies and prevent floods. In water-short areas, and those where storms wreak havoc, water security is more difficult and societies typically poorer.

There is also pressure on freshwater resources from population growth, urbanization, and increasingly industrialized lifestyles. In some desert settings, a traditionally well-adapted way of life has given way to water-profligacy – swimming pools, intensive irrigation – beyond the capacity of local renewable resources.

In some parts of the world, notably in Asia, the whole year's rainfall comes in a brief torrential season, complicating agricultural practice. The storage of water and its channelling via hydraulic infrastructure helps redress this problem. But there is a price to be paid by downstream populations, whose fishing or farming economies are jeopardized by major alterations in water pathways and flows.

Brazil

The Amazon region receives nearly 75% of Brazil's water, but is very lightly populated. The northeast coastal region, where 20% of people live, receives only 2%.

CHINA AND INDIA

Share of world renewable water resources and population *2014*

 water

population

Both China and India face extreme disparities between their share of the world's water and of its population, prompting China to propose ambitious projects to shift water between major rivers.

North America

All types of aridity zones are to be found in North America, and for millennia its indigenous peoples lived sustainably off the land. As European settlers moved across the country from east to west they also developed technologies that enabled them to survive in some of the harshest environments, but their use of the available water is not always sustainable in the long-term. Las Vegas, sprawling across the Nevada Desert, relies on the waters of the steadily shrinking Lake Mead.

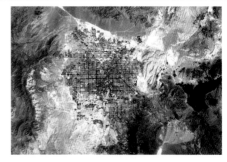

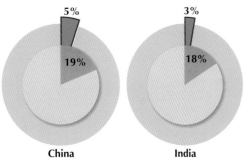

5%

19%

China

3%

18%

India

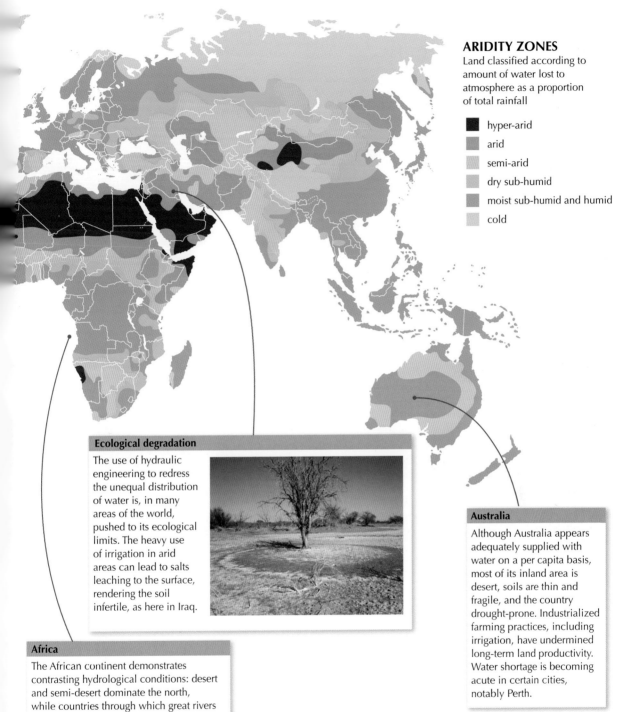

ARIDITY ZONES

Land classified according to amount of water lost to atmosphere as a proportion of total rainfall

- ■ hyper-arid
- ■ arid
- semi-arid
- dry sub-humid
- moist sub-humid and humid
- cold

Ecological degradation

The use of hydraulic engineering to redress the unequal distribution of water is, in many areas of the world, pushed to its ecological limits. The heavy use of irrigation in arid areas can lead to salts leaching to the surface, rendering the soil infertile, as here in Iraq.

Australia

Although Australia appears adequately supplied with water on a per capita basis, most of its inland area is desert, soils are thin and fragile, and the country drought-prone. Industrialized farming practices, including irrigation, have undermined long-term land productivity. Water shortage is becoming acute in certain cities, notably Perth.

Africa

The African continent demonstrates contrasting hydrological conditions: desert and semi-desert dominate the north, while countries through which great rivers flow are water-rich. One-third of Africa's population – 300 million people – live under conditions of water scarcity but geography and costs limit the prospects for major hydraulic infrastructure.

3 WATER SHORTAGE

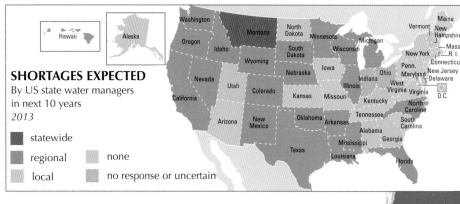

SHORTAGES EXPECTED
By US state water managers
in next 10 years
2013

- statewide
- regional
- local
- none
- no response or uncertain

The spectre of water shortage is less a global phenomenon than one threatening particular regions and localities. In areas under-endowed with rainfall or rivers, a combination of ever-increasing demand and, in some cases, less reliable rainfall, exacerbates the prospect of water shortage.

Water use grew at more than twice the rate of population increase in the last century. On current trends, by 2030 global freshwater withdrawals will exceed prospective reliable supplies by 40 per cent, with the disparity in some places being more than 50 per cent. At the same time, in some settings, water infrastructure and river diversion to fill reservoirs, irrigate crops and support industrialized lifestyles have already manipulated natural watercourses to the limits of possibility.

An increasing number of important rivers – including the Colorado (USA and Mexico), the Indus (India and Pakistan), the Huang He (China), the Rio Grande (North America and Mexico), and the Murray (Australia) – run dry, or almost do so, before they reach the sea for large parts of the year. Groundwater is also being pumped at rates that deplete aquifers and normal underground recharge into rivers and lakes.

Erratic weather patterns associated with climate change, in the form of multi-year droughts or altered monsoon behaviours, are also increasing the prospects of water shortage in vulnerable areas.

By 2025

4

billion
people will be living
in areas of
water stress

◀ *2 Water's Unequal Distribution*

POPULATION AND WATER

Annual renewable water resources
2014, China 2013
cubic metres per capita

■	fewer than 500 *absolute water scarcity*
■	500 – 999 *water scarcity*
■	1,000 – 1,699 *water stress*
■	1,700 – 2,499 *vulnerability*
■	2,500 or more *sufficient water*
■	10,000 or more *plentiful supplies*

Withdrawal as percentage of resources available:

💧 75% or more *absolute water scarcity*

💧 50% – 74% *water scarcity*

Water's uneven distribution is not only geographical. Human pressure on available supplies contributes to scarcity and stress.

Water stress in countries supplied from Himalayan sources

Population growth, economic expansion and rising living standards are exerting ever more pressure on supplies. In India, freshwater availability per capita has declined from over 4,000 cubic metres to 1,500 cubic metres in less than 50 years. In major river basins shared by Afghanistan, China, India and Pakistan there is strong competition between farmers, industrialists, and urban consumers and the potential for conflict. The depletion of water resources, when combined with annual and seasonal rainfall variability and vulnerability to drought and/or flood, creates severe water stress.

4 RISING DEMAND

More than 4,000 cubic kilometres of fresh water are withdrawn every year – equivalent to roughly 1,700 litres per person per day.

Although this is more than anyone needs for personal use, even to fill their swimming pool and sprinkle their garden round the clock, a large amount of water is consumed indirectly, embedded in food and industrial products. Meat-rich diets and other attributes of a high-consumption lifestyle, such as the acquisition of cars, television sets, and goods whose manufacturing processes require water, absorb ever larger quantities.

Thus, the rapid rise in demand, experienced across all categories of water use (agricultural, industrial, and domestic/municipal), is a reflection not just of an increasing global population but of changing lifestyles. Domestic use – for drinking, bathing, cleaning, – is modest compared to demand for agriculture and industry. But industrial water use, including that for hydropower, reflects people's demand for embedded water in the form of high-class products and high-end lifestyles. Those people still living in semi-subsistence economies make the lowest demands, often using fewer than 25 litres per person per day for all purposes.

Water for agriculture is by far the largest extractive category. This reflects lower demand for industrialized lifestyle items in less developed and more agrarian regions; and the dependence, in low rainfall and monsoon areas, on seasonal storage and irrigation from rivers, reservoirs and aquifers. Increasing demand for food and growing demand for energy continue to inspire heavy investment in large-scale water infrastructure, despite the costly ecological damage and human displacement entailed. Water withdrawals for irrigation are expected to increase by 5 per cent by 2050. This may sound modest, but will mainly occur in regions already suffering from water scarcity.

1900:

350
cubic metres

2000:

642
cubic metres
of water
used per capita
each year

WORLD WATER USE
by sector
2014

12% domestic

19% industry

69% agriculture

◀ 3 Water Shortage

HOW WATER IS USED

Proportion of water user per sector
in order of quantity withdrawn
Latest available 2000–13

- agriculture, industry, domestic/municipal
- agriculture, domestic/municipal, industry
- industry, agriculture, domestic/municipal
- industry, domestic, municipal/agriculture
- domestic/municipal, agriculture, industry
- domestic/municipal, industry, agriculture
- no data
- ▼ difference between first and second sector is 10 percentage points or less

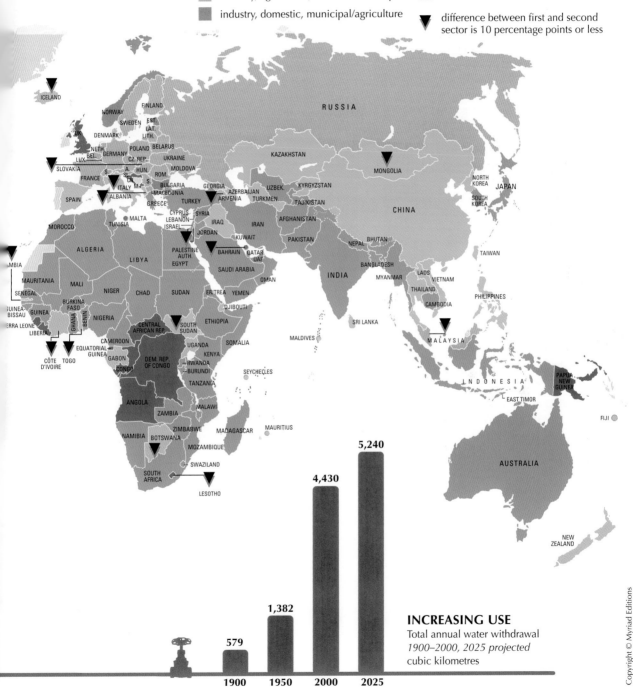

INCREASING USE

Total annual water withdrawal
1900–2000, 2025 projected
cubic metres

Year	Value
1900	579
1950	1,382
2000	4,430
2025	5,240

5 DWINDLING SUPPLY

1.5 billion
people rely on groundwater for their survival

982 cubic kilometres
of water is extracted from the ground each year

About a fifth of water consumed globally is from underground aquifers. These are replenished by rainwater seeping through soil and rock, but many are being over-exploited. Some non-renewable "fossil water" aquifers are being irreversibly mined.

In all parts of the world, groundwater is being withdrawn recklessly. The world's four top irrigators – China, India, Pakistan and the USA – are all pumping groundwater faster than it is being recharged. Twenty-one of the world's 37 largest aquifers are beyond their sustainability tipping point.

India is the largest groundwater user in the world, relying on it for 60 per cent of its irrigated agriculture. Cheap pumping technology and absence of fees and regulations have encouraged farmers to sink over 21 million tubewells. Some aquifers are now critically over-taxed, and existing wells constantly have to be deepened or replaced.

Similarly, in North Africa and the Arabian Peninsula, aquifers created during the last ice age are rapidly being sucked dry. Satellite mapping has shown the Arabian aquifer as the most stressed of all.

Many cities in Asia and the Americas rely on groundwater, which is preferred to surface water for drinking because it is less subject to contamination. However, heavy withdrawals lead to saltwater intrusion in coastal areas, turning the water supply brackish and unusable. Exhaustion of aquifers also causes land subsidence.

Aquifer recharge is now an important focus of sustainable groundwater management. In some water-scarce rural areas there has been a rediscovery of traditional recharge methods, such as rainwater harvesting, check-dams in stream beds and contour bunds on slopes to contain the run-off from precious downpours.

Denver, Colorado, USA

The 17,350 km² of the Denver Basin overlies a multi-layered aquifer system containing vast reserves of fossil water. Excessive pumping has lowered western basin water tables by 9 metres a year, threatening the viability of some sources by 2020.

Great Plains, USA

The Ogallala (High Plains) Aquifer underlies parts of eight US states, and yields 30% of the groundwater used for irrigation in the USA. In some parts of Kansas and Texas, decades of high-volume pumping have lowered the water table by up to 150 metres and flow is dwindling to the extent that irrigation is no longer possible.

Central Valley Aquifer, California

More than 100,000, mostly unregulated, wells suck water from the aquifer that runs under the Sacramento and San Joaquin valleys faster than it is replaced. The aquifer has been depleted by an estimated 25bn m³ since 2005, putting future irrigation into question.

Mexico City, Mexico

The extraction of water from aquifers at twice the rate of replenishment has led to some areas of the city subsiding at the rate of 2.5 cm a month.

GROUNDWATER

Type of aquifer and estimated annual recharge
2006

Major groundwater basin

- ■ high recharge
- ■ medium recharge
- ■ low recharge

Complex hydrogeological structure

- ■ high recharge
- ■ medium recharge
- ■ low recharge
- ■ local and shallow aquifers

Groundwater level average
annual decrease *2003–13*

- ⬇ 4–6 mm
- ⬇ 6–10 mm
- ⬇ 15–20 mm

Map courtesy WHYMAP. © BGR Hannover / UNESCO Paris 2006

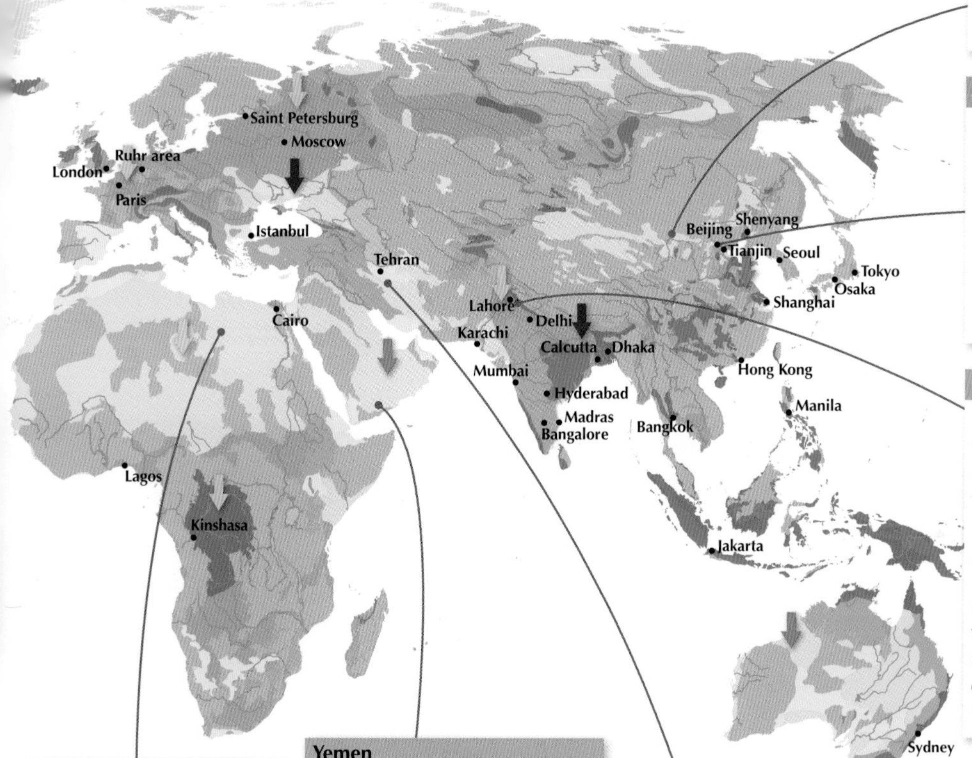

North China Plain

With 30 km³ more water being pumped out annually than is replaced, the water table is dropping at an alarming rate. Below the city of Shijiazhuang, wells have been drained of two-thirds of their water. In some areas, Chinese wheat farmers have to pump water 300 metres to the surface, making it uneconomical.

Beijing, China

Beijing has the sort of water scarcity normally associated with Saudi Arabia: 100 m³ per person a year. The water table under the city has dropped by 300 metres since the 1970s.

NW India and Pakistan

The Indus Basin aquifer is the second most overstressed in the world, with insufficient recharge. In 2002–12, farmers pumped out 8 per cent more water than was being replenished, causing water tables to drop by 1.4 metres a year. In some parts of Punjab, the annual drop is nearer 4 metres.

Libya

Water shortage is one of many current Libyan crises. Libya relies on groundwater for 95% of its supply, and annual recharge is only 250m m³ , whereas consumption is 1bn m³. Some aquifers, notably those tapped by the 1,000-km "Great Man-made River" from the depths of the Sahara, are non-renewable.

Yemen

Conflict-ridden Yemen is the poorest and most water-short country in the Middle East. Groundwater is the main source, but water tables have dropped severely. In Sana'a, the water table was at 30 metres below ground in the 1970s; by 2012, it was 1,200 metres down. 45% of groundwater is used to grow qat – a narcotic leaf. Experts suggest that Yemen may be the first country to run out of water.

Iran

Iran is over-pumping its aquifers by an average of 5bn m³ of water a year. Some villages in eastern Iran are being abandoned as wells run dry. Satellite mapping missions have recently shown an alarming decrease in total water in the Tigris–Euphrates basins and in Iran, mainly due to groundwater losses.

6 COMPETITION AND CONFLICT

As populations grow and more water is extracted, competition over the exploitation of rivers, lakes and aquifers increases. Where major water sources cross national boundaries, this can lead to political tension.

Many countries share rivers, and some depend heavily on water flowing in from elsewhere. When rivers are dammed or flows diverted in such a way as to benefit one population and deprive another, the potential for conflict increases sharply. The discharge of pollutants can also pit downstream against upstream inhabitants.

These pressures have led to talk of "water wars". So far, no war has been explicitly fought between nations over water, although occasional military, terrorist or activist strikes have been undertaken to destroy dams, cut off supplies or capture sites as part of a populist or other type of campaign. Sabre-rattling over some upstream hydraulic projects has also become increasingly noisy.

Water supplies feature strongly in some major political disputes, including that between Israel–Palestine. In Central Asia, confrontation has developed between six republics over what used to be a centralized dam and irrigation network in the days of the Soviet Union. In India, a dry year can lead to inter-state violence over ungenerous water releases by upstream states.

Competition between user groups with conflicting interests is not uncommon. Industrial users and farmers may dispute use of scarce resources, or companies with a commercial interest in water supplies may find themselves at loggerheads with local people who rely on the same supply for cultivating their basic crop.

Water disputes need to be solved at the basin-wide level, whether this is within one country but between states (as in India); or international, as in the case of the Nile and Indus. An increasing number of tribunals and river basin organizations have come into existence for this purpose.

Around

260

river basins

are shared by two or more countries

Nile Basin

The Nile is shared by Burundi, DR Congo, Egypt, Ethiopia, Kenya, Rwanda, South Sudan, Sudan, Tanzania and Uganda. Because it receives no run-off for 40% of its length, its flow is relatively small. Under a colonial-era agreement, downstream and dependent Egypt and Sudan were entitled to command of the Nile, causing upstream resentment. A Nile Basin Initiative is now trying to integrate the needs of all basin countries.

Bolivia–Chile

The waters of the Silala spring, Bolivia, flow through a canal westwards into Chile, where they are vital to the processing of copper in the Atacama desert. A disagreement over the natural course of this water prior to the construction of the canal in 1908 is part of a long-running territorial dispute. Bolivia claims that the water in the Silala Aquifer is its national property, the artificial canal is not governed by international water law, and Chile should pay Bolivia around $15,000 a day for the water. A draft bilateral agreement was rejected by Bolivia in 2010.

◄ 4 Rising Demand; 5 Dwindling Supply

ISIL in Iraq

ISIL recognizes the importance of controlling vital infrastructure in the battle to establish territorial control. In 2014 it temporarily closed the gates of the Fallujah Dam on the Euphrates, flooding farmland in an attempt to create a protective barrier for its forces, and also reducing the water supply to downstream, mainly Shiite, cities. It adopted a similar tactic in June 2015 in Ramadi. The brief control by ISIL of the huge Mosul Dam on the Tigris in August 2014 was a grave cause for concern. But although capturing dams gives ISIL a degree of power, in reality managing vast volumes of continually renewing water in a way that does not adversely impact on ISIL-controlled territory is a challenge.

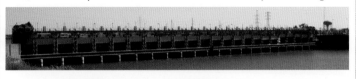

WATER DEPENDENCY

Percentage of renewable water resources originating from outside country
2014

- 75% or more
- 50% – 74%
- 25% – 49%
- less than 25% or no data

Countries with high dependency on sources from outside their own land mass are likely to be more vulnerable both to natural shortage and to conflict with upstream users.

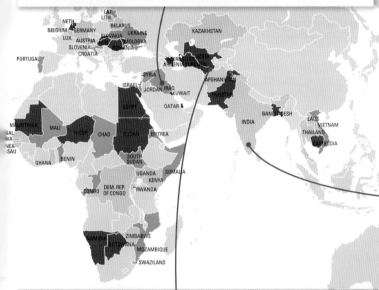

Kaveri River, India

Karnataka and Tamil Nadu States are obliged to share the waters of the Kaveri River. After a 50-year agreement ended in 1974, upstream Karnataka ceased its unwilling co-operation. Tamil Nadu's agricultural production depends on large-volume releases, but in a drought year, farmers in Karnataka become desperate and resolutely oppose the loss of "their" water. The government of India has stepped in on many occasions, setting up a dispute tribunal. But its "final" awards – most recently in 2013 – are invariably rejected by one state or both. Tensions can lead to disruptive violence.

Central Asia

The fertile areas of Central Asia are deserts made arable by an integrated system of dams and canals in the Syr Darya and Amu Darya basins, built in the Soviet era. Since then, management of the whole system has fractured – as have inter-state relations. The upstream states, Kyrgyzstan and Tajikistan, enjoy a water surplus, while Kazakhstan, Uzbekistan and Turkmenistan suffer, as the near-empty Aral Sea at the end of the rivers stands eloquent testimony. Infrastructure is dilapidated, and wasteful. Two new upstream dams proposed in 2012 ratcheted tensions further. Agreements are ignored and state leaders have so far proved immune to compromise.

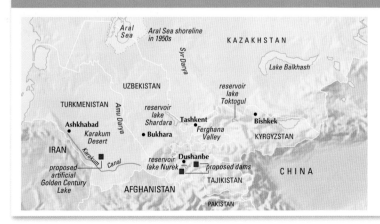

Just over

2
million km²
of the world's

12
million km²
wetlands
are protected

Aquatic ecosystems make a vital contribution to environmental security. Wetlands – bogs, swamps and marshes – maintain the viability of freshwater systems. Without them, rivers flow too fast, lakes become overburdened with organic matter, and coastlines are eroded.

Until recently, the essential services provided by freshwater ecosystems have been economically under-valued. Marshes detoxify wastewater, upland forests conserve water and soil and mangrove swamps protect the coastline from erosion and storm surges – problems worsening with climate change.

The loss of wetlands has been extensive. Around half of those in industrialized countries were destroyed before their importance was understood. They used to be seen as sources of "swamp fevers" such as malaria, and unproductive wet deserts that should be drained for settlement or agriculture. Some have been inundated or dried up as a result of dams altering river flows; others have had their water diverted for irrigation. Despite some reclamation, wetlands are deteriorating faster than any other ecosystem.

Their destruction has a devastating impact on those who live in them and off them. The freshwater fish in inland wetlands provide vital protein for millions of people in developing countries.

Attempts have been made to estimate the economic value of wetlands, some of which earn income from tourism and recreational activities as well as providing environmental benefits. In many cases, their worth turns out to be higher than that of the drained land.

Florida Everglades

The 2,000 km² of Florida's swamps represent only a fraction of their original size. In 1947, their ecological value was recognized by the creation of the Everglades National Park, but revival of the ecosystem has been stalled by the Florida sugar industry and farmers. In 2008, the Florida state government showed its commitment to ecological repair with a landmark decision to buy the US Sugar Corporation for $1.75 billion and use its land to restore flows of water to the Everglades from Lake Okeechobee.

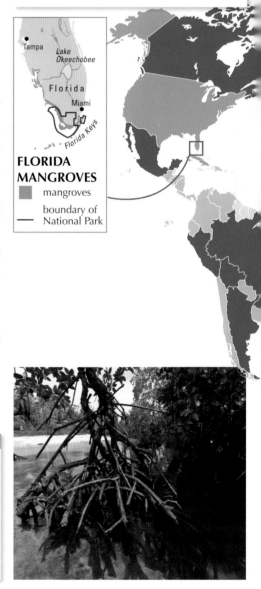

Tampa

Lake Okeechobee

Florida

Miami

Florida Keys

FLORIDA MANGROVES

◼ mangroves

— boundary of
National Park

The importance of mangroves

Mangroves are a unique group of trees and shrubs that grow only in coastal waters in tropical and subtropical latitudes. Their distinctive splayed roots slow down water flow, allowing sediments to accumulate. Hence mangrove forests protect mudflats and coasts and their root habitat attracts fish and other organisms seeking shelter. Degradation due to tourism, river-flow reduction, shrimp farming, and pesticide run-off continue to reduce the world's mangrove assets, exposing shorelines and coastal populations to the effects of violent storms.

PROTECTED WETLANDS

Area of protected wetlands in 169 countries that are signatories to Convention on Wetlands of International Importance (1971, Ramsar, Iran)
Oct 2015
square kilometres

- ■ 50,000 or more
- ■ 10,000 – 49,999
- ■ 1,000 – 9,999
- ■ fewer than 1,000
- ■ not a signatory

Total area protected: 2.1 million km²

Reconnecting lakes in the Yangtze basin

The wetland ecosystem of 1,066 lakes in Hubei Province traditionally played an important role in summer flood control in the Yangtze River basin. When 757 lakes were disconnected and converted to polders, massive flood damage resulted, causing hundreds of deaths and widespread economic loss. In 2002, under a WWF sustainable lake programme, sluice gates were seasonally opened around three major lakes, re-establishing natural flood protection and leading to a huge increase in fish, wildlife, and return of species. In 2006, Hubei province adopted a wetlands conservation plan and allocated resources to protect 4,500 km² by 2010.

Tonle Sap, Cambodia

People in Cambodia obtain up to 80% of their animal protein from fishing in the seasonal floodplains formed when the Mekong's flow is so strong that its tributary, the Tonle Sap, backs up into a huge lake. The future of the lake and fish stocks is precarious due to heavy damming of the Mekong.

FIJI ⊙

Inner Niger Delta, Mali

During the rainy season, the Niger and Bani rivers overspill their banks to form a 20,000 km² area of wetland, which supports fishers, farmers, and pastoralists in an otherwise arid country. Growing populations are competing to use the land, while limited rainfall and the damming of the Niger have reduced water levels.

Southern Iraq

Once a richly diverse habitat of 20,000 km², supporting a population of 250,000 Ma'dan or Marsh Arabs, the marshlands of Southern Iraq were depleted first in the 1970s by dams on the Tigris and Euphrates, and then destroyed by Saddam Hussein. In the 1990s, he carried out extensive drainage and diversion schemes in retaliation against a Ma'dan insurrection. Around 175,000 people were killed or displaced, leaving a salt-pan desert. Since Saddam's fall, there has been a scientifically managed attempt at marshland rehabilitation, led by Iraqi environmentalists. Half the area has been re-flooded, but life there remains fragile.

Tigris
IRAN
Al'Amarah
IRAQ
Al-Hawizeh Marsh
An Nasiriyah
Al Qurnah
Euphrates
Al Basrah
0   100 km

RECOVERING THE GARDEN OF EDEN

Changing extent of the marshlands of southern Iraq

- ⬚ marshland in 1973
- ■ marshland in 2002
- ■ marshland restored since 2003

PART 2   WATER AND CLIMATE CHANGE

Water plays a central role in the protection and health of our environment, from the level of atmospheric and meteorological forces, down to the intimate context of homes and communities. Thus the ways climate change interacts with the forces that govern freshwater supplies on the planet run the gamut from variations in rain and snowfall and when and where they fall, to rises in seawater and freshwater temperatures; and to the ways in which these changes affect the aquatic environment and all forms of human activity and economic production.

The latest report of the International Panel on Climate Change is unequivocal in its findings that the climate system has warmed, and that many of the observed changes since the 1950s are unprecedented over decades to millennia. The atmosphere and ocean have warmed, the amounts of snow and ice have diminished, and sea level has risen. In the past two decades, the Greenland and Antarctic ice sheets have been losing mass, at a rate that appears to be speeding up.

The changes in rainfall and snowfall, and the melting of ice, are the most noticeable effects of climate change, and their impact on the water resources that support human life and make possible the planetary food basket, both natural and specifically cultivated, is the most profound of all impacts. Many terrestrial, freshwater and marine species have shifted their geographic ranges, migration patterns, seasonal activities and abundance in response to climate change. Some areas have seen higher crop yields, but negative effects are more common.

Catastrophic droughts and floods – disasters that used to be seen purely as the product of natural forces – are becoming more common. The growing season of 2014 was seriously affected by drought in Ethiopia, southern Africa, and in Central America, due to record global temperatures. Soaring temperatures in 2015 led to the strongest El Niño on record, a climate phenomenon that develops in the tropical Pacific and brings extreme weather to many regions.

These impacts on the hydrological environment have to be added to other human factors relating to the management and use of water resources that feed into environmental stress. In many river basins, alterations in natural flows have led to losses of plant and fish species and various forms of damage to upstream and downstream ecosystems. Threats of pollution associated with rising levels of industrialization and urbanization will be augmented by flow alterations due to climate change.

The need to factor climate-change impacts into environmental protection and freshwater conservation, and to balance all three with the rising demands on water supplies, is of paramount importance to the future survival and health of humanity.

8 ICE AND SNOW MELT

THINNING

Regional average annual change in mass balance *1996–2005* metres of water equivalent

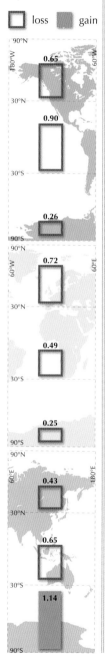

loss □   gain ■

0.65

0.90

0.26

0.72

0.49

0.25

0.43

0.65

1.14

Climate change affects glaciers, ice-sheets, permafrost, snow-melt volume and rates, and therefore river flow, in many complex ways.

An increase in global temperatures influences the whole hydrological cycle, affecting when and how much rain and snow is precipitated, and where. Northern latitudes are likely to receive more precipitation, both rain and snow; those in mid-latitudes less.

Rising temperatures are also accelerating a process already underway in the world's extreme latitudes, and in high mountain ranges: the melting of ice-caps and reduction of snow on high peaks. Most of the world's glaciers are retreating, some at rapid rates, meaning that their summer melt is higher than the winter replenishment of snow and ice.

The Greenland and Antarctic ice-sheets contain 99 per cent of the freshwater ice on Earth. The loss of their ice, by more summer melting than re-freezing, "calving" of icebergs and break-up of ice shelves, is sometimes described as 'a canary in a coalmine' in that it indicates climate changes before they are experienced elsewhere. Changes in the cryosphere – the ice-bound part of the world – are therefore acknowledged as important for many reasons.

Up in the Himalayas, a 60-square-kilometre area of ice and glaciers contains the sources of rivers that, during their flow, supply much of the population of India, China and nearby countries. Changes in the volume and timing of the water flowing from these sources is already affecting the populations of the river basins through which they pass on their way to the sea.

Rises in sea level have an important impact on people living on low-lying islands and archipelagos, deltas and coasts.

North America

The Columbia River, the largest in Pacific NW America, rises high in the Rocky Mountains of British Columbia, and is dependent on snow-melt for its flow. The warmer climate has decreased the spring snowpack and flow peaks earlier in the year, reducing the level and raising the temperature of the river. This threatens the survival of salmon, central to the food and culture of local indigenous tribes. Over 250,000 salmon in the basin died from overheating in 2015.

South America

The Andes run for 7,000 km, making it the longest continental mountain chain in the world. Its extensive glaciated areas are a vital source of ice-melt for rivers relied on by millions of people, especially in tropical and semi-tropical zones. Except for a few in Patagonia, Andean glaciers are in retreat. The tropical glaciers have declined at an unprecedented rate, losing between 35% and 50% of their volume in 30 years.

Antarctica

Antarctica's ice-sheet is vast, covering 14m km². The temperature there has risen by 3°C in the last 50 years, 10 times faster than the global average. This has not affected the main low-temperature mass, but at the Western edge, where floating ice-shelves extend out over the warmer water along the Antarctic Peninsula, many ice-shelves have collapsed. New research predicts a rapid increase in this melting.

Greenland

The Greenland ice-sheet covers 1.7m km², a much smaller area than that in Antarctica, and its temperature is warmer thanks to Pacific currents entering via the Bering Strait. Climate change has had a huge effect on its ice. Summer sea-ice volume is less than a quarter of what it was a generation ago, and may vanish completely by 2050. White ice melting into dark water inhibits Earth's ability to reflect light and heat back into space, potentially increasing overall warming.

The European Alps

Glaciers in the Alps are both retreating and diminishing in overall mass, and in many places the pace of change is accelerating. This is projected to reduce Europe's hydropower capacity by 6% by the 2070s – bad news for countries such as Switzerland, which generates half of its electricity in this way.

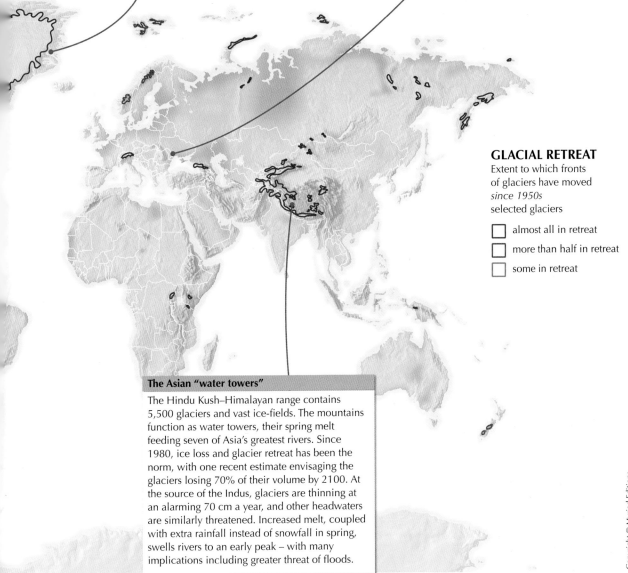

GLACIAL RETREAT

Extent to which fronts
of glaciers have moved
since 1950s
selected glaciers

☐ almost all in retreat

☐ more than half in retreat

☐ some in retreat

The Asian "water towers"

The Hindu Kush–Himalayan range contains 5,500 glaciers and vast ice-fields. The mountains function as water towers, their spring melt feeding seven of Asia's greatest rivers. Since 1980, ice loss and glacier retreat has been the norm, with one recent estimate envisaging the glaciers losing 70% of their volume by 2100. At the source of the Indus, glaciers are thinning at an alarming 70 cm a year, and other headwaters are similarly threatened. Increased melt, coupled with extra rainfall instead of snowfall in spring, swells rivers to an early peak – with many implications including greater threat of floods.

9 STORMS AND FLOODS

Cost of
flood damage
in 2014
in Asia:

$29
billion

Climate change is leading to an increasing number of extreme weather events, including more intense rainfall and violent storms. Devastating floods are becoming more frequent.

Two types of meteorological event trigger flooding. One is prolonged or heavy rainfall or rapid seasonal snow-melt, which over-fills river basins, spilling streams beyond their banks and natural floodplains. The other is storms that force the sea inland and breach flood defences. All are becoming more frequent and more intense due to global warming.

However, alterations to the environment, such as draining of wetlands and constraint of rivers by dams and embankments, are also significant. More than 6.9 million hectares of wetlands alongside the Mississippi – the river's natural sponge – have been drained and developed over the past 100 years. These are now prone to severe flooding in a rainy year.

Deforestation also exacerbates flood disasters. Rainfall on treeless slopes washes away soil that would previously have absorbed it. This not only causes landslides, but increases the input of water and silt to rivers; and reduces the volume of water that can be held in watercourses and reservoirs.

Low-lying countries are especially vulnerable. Some delta areas depend on the fertile silt deposited by the annual flood of major rivers. One-third of Bangladesh is routinely flooded, but if there is too much rain, or a cyclone coincides, the fragile blessings of flood transform into disaster.

Floods in cities are worsened by impermeable concrete or tarmac preventing rain from soaking into the ground. Flashfloods in such cities as Mumbai, with torrential rainfall unable to exit through blocked drains, have become regular occurrences.

El Niño

The El Niño effect occurs every few years to a varying degree. Easterly winds in the South Pacific weaken, allowing warm water, accompanied by rain, to move eastward. Peru, Ecuador and the southern USA typically experience increased rainfall, and weather patterns all over the globe are affected. A particularly strong El Niño effect was recorded in July 2015.

RISING WATERS
Number of floods worldwide
1995–14

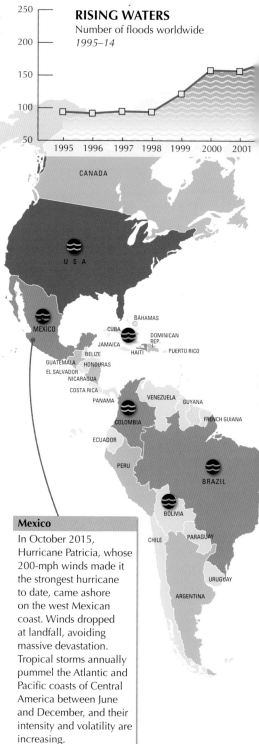

Mexico

In October 2015, Hurricane Patricia, whose 200-mph winds made it the strongest hurricane to date, came ashore on the west Mexican coast. Winds dropped at landfall, avoiding massive devastation. Tropical storms annually pummel the Atlantic and Pacific coasts of Central America between June and December, and their intensity and volatility are increasing.

◄ 7 Environmental Security; 8 Ice and Snow Melt

STORMS AND FLOODS
Number of storms, floods and landslides
2000–14

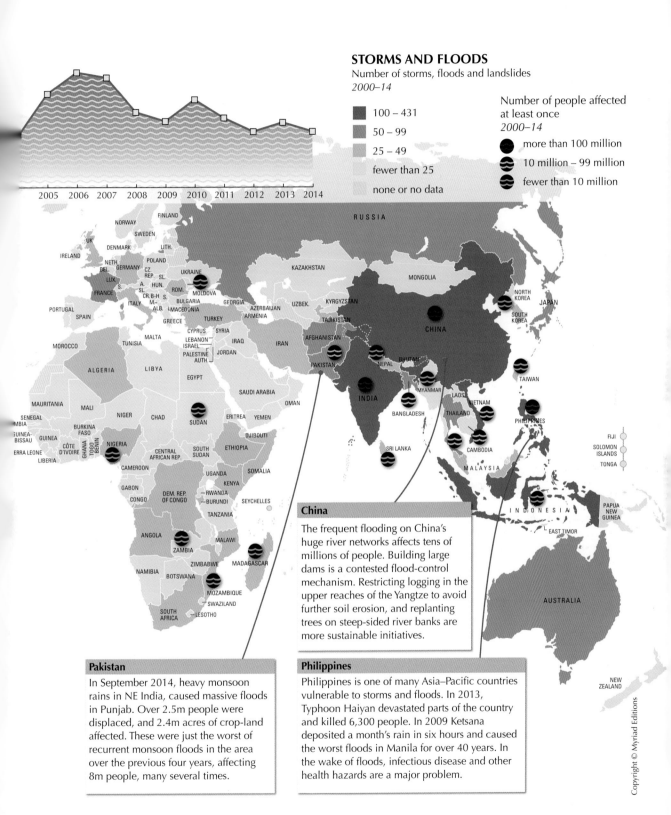

■	100 – 431
■	50 – 99
■	25 – 49
	fewer than 25
	none or no data

Number of people affected
at least once
2000–14

● more than 100 million

◐ 10 million – 99 million

◯ fewer than 10 million

China
The frequent flooding on China's huge river networks affects tens of millions of people. Building large dams is a contested flood-control mechanism. Restricting logging in the upper reaches of the Yangtze to avoid further soil erosion, and replanting trees on steep-sided river banks are more sustainable initiatives.

Pakistan
In September 2014, heavy monsoon rains in NE India, caused massive floods in Punjab. Over 2.5m people were displaced, and 2.4m acres of crop-land affected. These were just the worst of recurrent monsoon floods in the area over the previous four years, affecting 8m people, many several times.

Philippines
Philippines is one of many Asia–Pacific countries vulnerable to storms and floods. In 2013, Typhoon Haiyan devastated parts of the country and killed 6,300 people. In 2009 Ketsana deposited a month's rain in six hours and caused the worst floods in Manila for over 40 years. In the wake of floods, infectious disease and other health hazards are a major problem.

10 DROUGHTS

The world's drylands will become drier as a result of climate change. As temperatures rise, increased evapotranspiration from land, seas and plants reinforces aridity and desertification. Heatwaves will become more extreme, and droughts more frequent and last for longer periods.

Drylands cover 41 per cent of the world's land area. At their extreme, they are deserts where people are few and life very tough. But drylands also include habitats such as rangelands, savannahs and oases, and are thus home to 40 per cent of the world's people – 2.1 billion – two-thirds of whom live in Asia.

Many nomadic peoples, in dry cold zones such as Siberia and Mongolia, as well as in hot deserts such as the Sahara, migrate with the seasons to exploit scarce water and grazing effectively. But their lifestyles are fragile, and a prolonged multi-year drought can decimate their herds and threaten starvation.

Even without the extra threats posed by climate change, drylands have been under increasing pressure, due to population increase and poor land and water management. Unrestrained use of aquifers, and the damming and diversion of river waters to improve farming prospects and yields, has led to a build-up of herd size, over-grazing, loss of vegetative cover and topsoil erosion. Ironically, this can make drylands more susceptible to flash floods in the rainy season.

These practices themselves lead to rises in temperature and reductions in rainfall due to the loss of moisture in the soil, thus reinforcing the negative impacts of temperature rise. The livelihoods of around 1 billion people in around 100 countries are threatened by dryland degradation, mainly due to reduced availability of water and the desertification of marginal cropland. By 2030, water scarcity in arid and semi-arid areas will mean that between 24 million and 700 million people will be displaced from dryland habitats.

24%
of dryland area
supporting
1.5
billion
people
is degrading

California, USA

In January 2015, California Governor Gerry Brown declared a state of emergency in the face of a multi-year record-breaking drought, which had drastically depleted reservoirs and lakes and killed off 12 million trees, increasing the risk of wildfires. Strict water conservation measures threatened heavy fines for wasteful water use, prompting disuse of swimming pools and landscape-greening hoses. However, in winter 2015/16 California experienced severe flooding thanks to a strong El Niño.

Central America

In the dry corridor running through Guatemala, Honduras and El Salvador, 3.5 million people were affected by drought in 2015, caused by the El Niño event that elsewhere was causing floods. Most farming families live at the margins, and their resilience crumbled in the face of the complete loss of their staple maize and bean crops, and the death of their cattle.

Gobi Desert

China's food and water supplies are vulnerable to drought and to desertification, with 400 million people struggling with water shortages, unproductive land, and ecological systems disrupted by high temperatures. Encroaching deserts herald their advance with sandstorms that reach even into the heart of cities. The Gobi desert is annually swallowing up around 3,600 km² on its way to Beijing.

Pacific Islands

Small islands that rely on rainfall for fresh water are especially vulnerable. The El Niño of 2015 brought very dry conditions in the southwest Pacific, including on Papua New Guinea, Tonga and the Solomon Islands, and the already drought-affected Fiji. Up to 4.1 million people faced food and water shortages.

DROUGHTS

Number
2000–14

- 20
- 5 – 8
- 3 – 4
- 1 – 2
- none recorded

East Africa

A series of drought years caused extreme hardship in the Horn of Africa, climaxing in 2011, when livestock died, harvests failed and staple food prices soared. In 2014, Kenya declared a drought emergency, with 1.6 million dryland herders and farmers in marginal areas affected. As these countries struggle to deal with repeated weak annual rains, 2015–16 threated too much rain, floods and storm damage to crops, as a result of the strong El Niño of 2015.

Australia

The aboriginal people of Australia lived lightly on the land of this dry continent. Post-settlement industrialized farming systems and urban development requires plentiful supplies of water and are proving hard to sustain. Evidence suggests that climate change is making drought conditions in southwest and southeast Australia worse. The average annual flow into Perth's dams has fallen by 80% since the 1970s, and over-pumping of aquifers has led to the city's subsidence by 2–6 mm a year.

11 RIVER BASIN STRESSES

2016:

21
million

2030:

54
million
people could be
affected by
river floods

The increased volatility of rainfall and river flow, and higher temperatures of fresh water in lakes and streams, have important impacts on river basin networks. These affect water quantities at different times of year, as well as water quality.

These changes will both exacerbate existing environmental stresses, and increase tensions already created by rising demands on water exerted by population growth and urbanization in overstretched river basins. Where users already compete for scarce supplies, changes in the volume, variability and seasonality of run-off will sharpen competition. In some major river basins, variability from year to year and season to season, already large, is becoming more acute.

Since irrigated farming accounts for 70 per cent of water withdrawals from rivers and lakes, agriculture will be the sector most affected by climate change, and the one most challenged to adopt new techniques that conserve water.

Climate change will also worsen the quality of surface fresh water. Flooding washes sediment into rivers, bringing with it pathogens, residue from pesticides, heavy metals from industry, and phosphorus, which, combined with warmer water, can result in algal blooms.

In urban areas, floods also cause sewage systems to overflow, contaminating the streets and infiltrating drinking-water supplies. Heavier rainfall churns up reservoirs, increasing turbidity and requiring extra treatment. Where river flows are seasonally more reduced, pollutants are concentrated in the remaining water.

All these effects are likely to have negative effects on the health, not only of people, but of entire ecosystems. In addition, as warmer oceans expand, sealevel will rise, not only inundating land, but introducing salt into freshwater coastal aquifers.

SELECTED BASINS AT RISK

The World Resources Institute focused on the 100 largest and most heavily populated river basins and assessed their risk of different types of water stress:

Baseline stress: ratio of annual withdrawals to annual renewable supply

Inter-annual variability: fluctuations in flow and water level from year to year

Seasonal variability: large fluctuations from season to season

Flood occurrence: numbers of floods

Drought severity: numbers and severity of droughts

Water risk scores

■ 4–5 extremely high

▨ 3–3.9 high

▨ 2–2.9 medium to high

▨ 1–1.9 low to medium

□ 0–1 low

Colorado River

The waters of the Colorado are shared by seven US states and Mexico. It is already undergoing a sustained period of drought and its flow is predicted to decline by 9% or more within 50 years due to climate change. The population of 33 million it currently supports in terms of drinking water, irrigation and hydropower is expected to increase by 33% or more over the same period. This could lead to an excess of demand for water over supply of around 4.3bn m³ (roughly a quarter of its natural flow) by mid-century.

Ganges–Brahmaputra

The Ganges and Brahmaputra are one of the largest river systems on Earth. Both rise in the Himalayas, the Ganges in India on the southern slopes, and the Brahmaputra on the northern, running along the Tibetan plateau through China as the Tsangbo River before turning south. The two rivers join in Bangladesh, where they enter the Bay of Bengal. The whole basin is just over 1.6 million km², and the combined delta has the highest population density of any in the world. Thus, seasonal variation in the flow of these two rivers is critical to the lives of hundreds of millions of people, whose staple food crops may be over-inundated in one year and dry out in another.

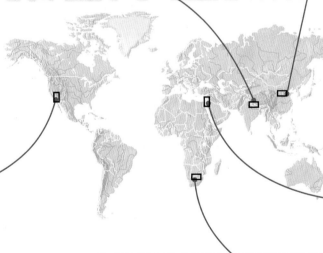

Mouths of the Ganges

Huang He

The volume of water that flows down the Huang He (Yellow River) to the delta has decreased every decade since the 1970s. Warmer temperatures and reduced precipitation in the northeast Loess Plateau watershed are one cause. The other is increasing demands from agriculture, industry, and the 12% of China's population who live in its basin. The proportion of its flow diverted for irrigation has grown from 20% to around 70% since the 1960s, and reservoirs constructed to regulate the river's flow have led to loss of water through evaporation.

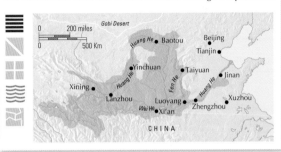

Dead Sea (Jordan River)

The Dead Sea is well-named. With a shoreline at the lowest land point on the globe – 423 metres below sea level – and no outlet, millennia of evaporation have left the seabed caked in minerals and the water eight times saltier than the sea. Fresh water used to flow in from the Jordan River, but in recent years its flow has dwindled dramatically, with Israel extracting 65% of the Upper Jordan's water and piping it south for use in arid coastal regions. New pressures on the trickling Jordan River have come from the hundreds of thousands of refugees from Syria, camping in arid and water-impoverished Jordan.

Zambezi

The Zambezi river basin is the fourth largest in Africa. It runs through eight countries and is home to 45 million people. The Zambezi is also one of the most heavily dammed rivers in Africa, with four of the world's largest hydroelectric dams. These are vulnerable to seasonal variability in rainfall and flow, which leads to reductions in power generation as well as river degradation. Large reservoirs are also sources of greenhouse gases.

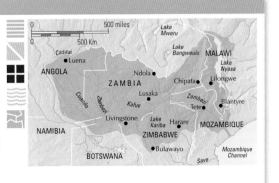

PART 3   WATER FOR LIVING

Drinking water is even more vital for human survival than food. And if a water supply is not safe to drink, instead of being the source of life, water becomes a potential source of life-threatening disease. In today's crowded world, wells and streams that used to be potable have become contaminated with bacteria or other pollutants.

Hence the tremendous effort over recent decades to supply everyone on Earth with a safe, convenient and reliable drinking-water supply. A piped supply to the home or, failing that, protected wells and springs to nearby locations, are greatly valued by communities everywhere, and help control the spread of disease. Their use in hygienic practices, especially handwashing, is as important in this connection as for safe drinking.

Thus the amount of water essential for domestic use is far greater than that required purely for drinking. Water is needed for cooking, bathing, washing-up, laundry, flushing the toilet and sometimes also for watering small livestock and vegetable plots. Providing adequate piped supplies for every household, especially if treated to drinking-water standards, is extremely expensive, which explains why 683 million people are still hauling water from a deficient source.

Most people in developing countries have to manage on much less water than those in industrialized countries, and the poor typically work harder and pay more for their supply than the better-off. They are also much less likely to have a tap or flush toilet in the home, let alone a piped connection to a drain or sewerage system.

Large quantities of water are consumed in the form of food. Edible plants are either nourished by rain-fed moisture in the soil, or by water channelled from surface or underground sources. Every calorie we eat requires for cultivation an average of a litre of water.

The production of food per head has risen steadily in recent decades, mainly due to intensive planting of high-yield crop strains under irrigation. This expansion in staple food production has been a successful response to the basic needs of rising populations.

However, lifestyle choices also play a part. Many of those who have improved their living standards in countries such as China, India and Indonesia now eat meat and poultry products in much greater quantity than before. All of these absorb far more water per kilo of production than basic starchy staples, such as potatoes or wheat. This is an additional source of pressure on water supplies, and is reflected in the rising price of many foodstuffs.

12 WATER FOR DRINKING

683
million
still use an open or unimproved drinking water source

319
million
of whom are in Africa

Everyone has access to a source of drinking water – otherwise they could not survive. But natural 'unimproved' sources such as streams and open wells are often contaminated by human and animal waste.

In our increasingly crowded world, access to safe drinking water requires that the supplies people use for domestic purposes reach public health standards described as "improved". These include public taps, protected boreholes, and tanks filled by springs or rainwater. They should be convenient, meaning in the house or yard or close to the home, potable and reliable. This requires public health engineering (drilling, laying pipes, tank construction), which means that water – a naturally occurring, free public good – incurs a cost. The service has to be paid for somehow.

Today, 91 per cent of people use an improved drinking-water source. In rural areas, the proportion is 84 per cent; in towns, it rises to 96 per cent. However, urban access is often seriously deficient. Townspeople may be assessed as fully covered when taps or standpipes are installed every 200 metres, and users are obliged to share with hundreds of other households. Village taps or pumps at similar distances serve far fewer people and are far less likely to break down.

Those without a water connection at their home often fetch water from a distance. Traditionally, women haul water – an extremely heavy substance – adding a considerable burden to the daily workload. In many African countries, the round-trip to the source takes more than 30 minutes, restricting the amount that can be brought home. Since this water has to be used for laundering clothes, cooking and watering small livestock, as well as for drinking, personal hygiene typically suffers.

WATER ACCESS
Percentage of population using water from different sources
1990 & 2015

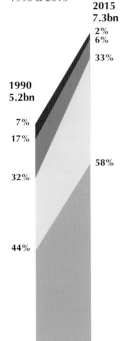

2015
7.3bn
2%
6%
33%
58%

1990
5.2bn
7%
17%
32%
44%

■ **surface water**
• open river or stream

■ **unimproved**
• unprotected well or spring
• water cart or tanker

□ **improved**
• public tap or standpipe
• borehole / tubewell
• protected well or spring
• protected rainwater tank

■ **piped to premises**
• piped water to dwelling or yard

CANADA

U S A

MEXICO
BAHAMAS
CUBA
DOMINICAN REP.
HAITI
PUERTO RICO
JAMAICA
BELIZE
GUATEMALA HONDURAS
EL SALVADOR
NICARAGUA
COSTA RICA
PANAMA
ST KITTS & NEVIS
ST VINCENT & GRENAD.
GRENADA
VENEZUELA
COLOMBIA
ECUADOR
PERU
BOLIVIA
CHILE
PARAGUAY
BRAZIL
URUGUAY
ARGENTINA
ANTIGUA & BARBUD
ST LUCIA
BARBADOS
TRINIDAD & TOBAGO
GUYANA
SURINAME

In Sub-Saharan Africa, where 75% of people still have no household water connection, fetching water mostly falls to women and girls.

WATER COLLECTION
2006–09

boys
6%
girls
9%
men
23%
women
62%

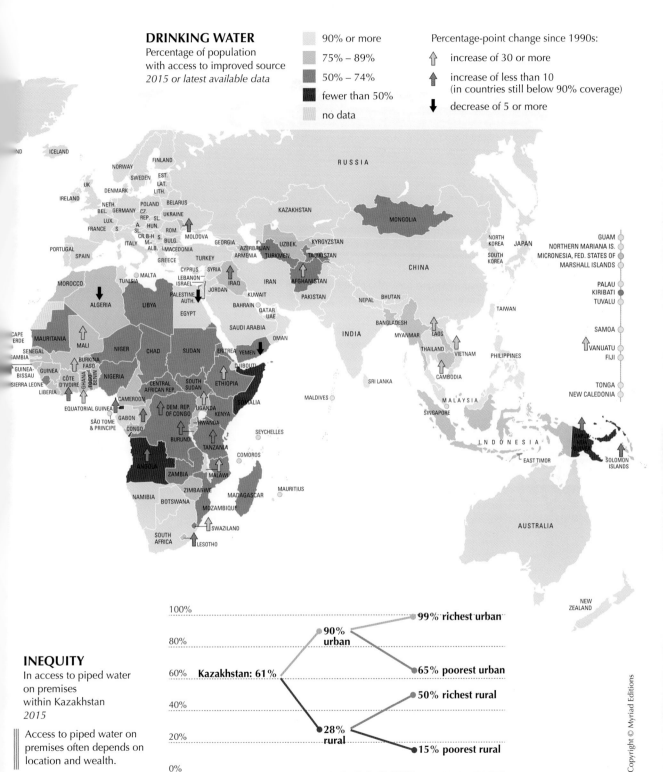

DRINKING WATER

Percentage of population
with access to improved source
2015 or latest available data

- 90% or more
- 75% – 89%
- 50% – 74%
- fewer than 50%
- no data

Percentage-point change since 1990s:

- ⬆ increase of 30 or more
- ⬆ increase of less than 10
  (in countries still below 90% coverage)
- ⬇ decrease of 5 or more

INEQUITY

In access to piped water
on premises
within Kazakhstan
2015

Access to piped water on
premises often depends on
location and wealth.

Kazakhstan: 61%

- 99% richest urban
- 90% urban
- 65% poorest urban
- 50% richest rural
- 28% rural
- 15% poorest rural

13 WATER FOR FOOD

CHANGING DIET IN CHINA

Weight of meat and milk purchased annually by urban dwellers
1990–2012

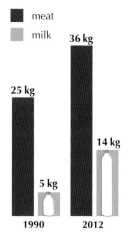

■ meat
■ milk

25 kg

36 kg

5 kg

14 kg

1990   2012

All food production depends on water, either falling as rain and moistening the soil to enable plants to grow, or drawn from rivers, lakes and aquifers. Thus, stress on water resources means stress on the global and family food basket.

Historically, agriculture was at the whim of climate and environment – and in large parts of the world, notably in Africa, it still is. In rain-short areas, the fertility provided by rivers and wetlands has to be carefully exploited. Crops were – and are – grown on floodplains when waters recede. Even in Biblical times, earthen dams corralled water into reservoirs, and canals, and lifting devices were constructed to channel water to where it was needed. Growing food has always been about creative manipulation of water, on a family and on a wider social basis.

Food production has grown dramatically in recent decades, not just in response to population growth but also to meet rising overall demand, driven by increased incomes. By 2050, demand for food is predicted to increase by 60 per cent, and by 100 per cent in developing countries.

Higher standards of living, such as those seen among the new urban middle-class in China, have been accompanied by changing diets, with people eating more meat, poultry and dairy products. Even in the USA, where beef has long been top of the menu, demand is still rising. Beef cattle reared on a feed lot, consuming grain for three years, each consume an estimated 3 million litres of water from birth to slaughter.

Irrigation and high-yielding crop strains provided a 20th-century golden bullet for increasing food supplies. But the downside now weighs heavily. Aquifers are depleted and river flows reduced by inefficient usage, while wildlife – a traditional food source – has been decimated.

Many small farmers, notably in Africa, need better access to water supplies in the dry season to improve family food security. When it comes to water for food, small-scale is as important as large-scale, as water constraints lead to higher prices for water-thirsty foodstuffs.

A western diet requires around

3,500

litres
per day
to produce

15,415

Large amounts of water are needed to produce common foodstuffs. Meat of all kinds requires high volumes, while vegetables and fruit require much less.

5,988

4,325

2,497

1,608

822

287   237   214

WATER FOR FOOD

Average number of litres of water needed to produce 1 kilogram
2013

beef   pork   chicken   rice   bread   apple   potatoes   cabbage   tomato

◄ 2 Water's Unequal Distribution

WATER FOR AGRICULTURE

Amount withdrawn from rivers and aquifers
for agricultural use
latest available data 2000–14
cubic metres per person per year

1,000 or more	100 – 249
500 – 999	under 100
250 – 499	no data

By 2050 a
19%
increase
in agricultural
water consumption
is expected

SOURCE OF WATER
FOR AGRICULTURE

"blue water"
rivers and aquifers

"green water"
rainfall

12%
88%
Latin America

17%
83%
OECD countries

39%
61%
**Middle East &
North Africa**

6%
94%
**Sub-Saharan
Africa**

20%
80%
**Central Asia &
Eastern Europe**

41%
59%
South Asia

22%
78%
East Asia

Copyright © Myriad Editions

14 WATER FOR SANITATION

**2.4
billion**
people lack
improved
sanitation facilities

In the industrialized world, water is a critical ingredient for flushing toilets, as well as a vehicle for flushing dirt into drains and into waterways. Stormwater drains also act as conduits for the removal of surplus rainwater and snowmelt.

Conventional sewerage typically requires 15,000 litres per person per year for flushing. The provision of such a service is technically unfeasible in almost all rural and many poor urban environments in developing countries. It would also be prohibitively expensive: costs vary from $400 to $1,500 per head, rising steeply if provision is also made for sewage treatment.

One alternative is dry sanitation systems: using pits or tanks for storing excreta safe from human contact, and in some cases reusing composted material as fertilizer. Some pit toilets have an S-bend "water seal", and are flushed by hand with a small bucket of water.

Various models of toilet are regarded as "improved" according to public health definitions, but no distinction is made in coverage data between "wet" and "dry" varieties. Most people prefer a water-seal toilet as more salubrious, but dry systems are used in some water-short areas, notably in China.

**90%
of sewage**
in developing
countries is
discharged
untreated into
watercourses

In developing-world cities, regular sewerage only serves a small elite, but its output is often discharged straight into rivers. In some urban environments, a simplified form of sewerage has been developed, using smaller-diameter pipes and community construction and maintenance. This reduces costs to between $50 and $260 a head. This approach has been used quite extensively in Central and South America.

Wastewater services are universally needed – for greywater (water used for cooking, laundry and bathing), blackwater (sewage) and stormwater run-off, which otherwise collects as standing water and breeds insects, including malarial mosquitoes. Given the impossibility of introducing industrialized world wastewater treatment in large parts of the developing world, local management of wastewater is the realistic alternative.

Constructed wetland for wastewater treatment

The Arcata Wetlands, constructed on former industrial land, contributes to the treatment of the domestic wastewater of 18,000 citizens in Arcata, California. After solid matter has been removed (primary treatment), the water passes through oxidation ponds (secondary treatment), which reduces the Biochemical Oxygen Demand (BOD) by 50%, before the water is released into the wetlands. Constructed wetlands on a smaller scale are increasingly being associated with new housing or office developments.

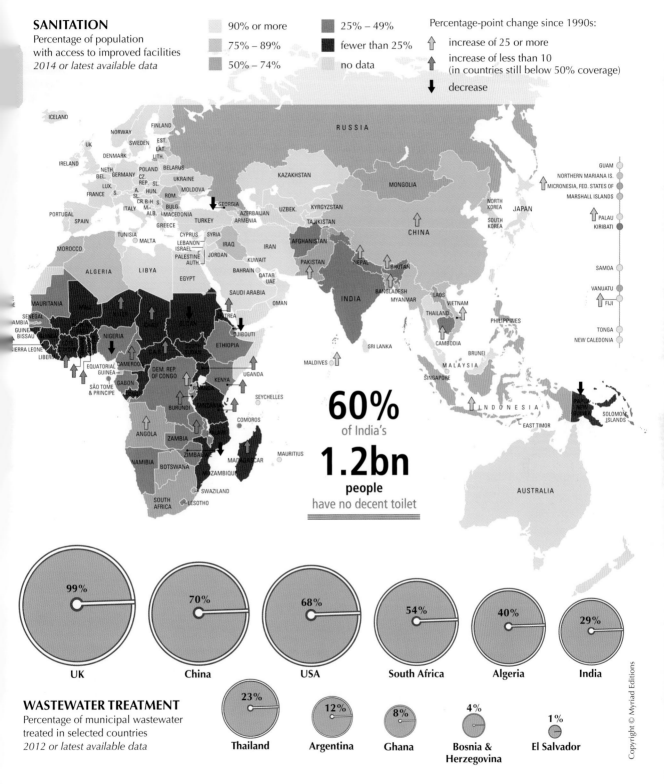

SANITATION

Percentage of population
with access to improved facilities
2014 or latest available data

- 90% or more
- 75% – 89%
- 50% – 74%
- 25% – 49%
- fewer than 25%
- no data

Percentage-point change since 1990s:

- ⇧ increase of 25 or more
- ⇧ increase of less than 10
  (in countries still below 50% coverage)
- ⬇ decrease

60%
of India's
1.2bn
people
have no decent toilet

WASTEWATER TREATMENT

Percentage of municipal wastewater
treated in selected countries
2012 or latest available data

Country	Percentage
UK	99%
China	70%
USA	68%
South Africa	54%
Algeria	40%
India	29%
Thailand	23%
Argentina	12%
Ghana	8%
Bosnia & Herzegovina	4%
El Salvador	1%

15 WATER IN THE CITY

828
million
urban dwellers
live in slums

Since 2008, more people live in towns and cities than in the countryside. The rapid growth of urban populations exerts huge pressures on municipal infrastructure and service provision, especially in poorer parts of the world.

In urban spaces with exceptionally high population growth, the authorities are constantly playing catch-up. Much existing infrastructure is already inefficient: one-third of the water supply in many systems is lost to leakage. Flooding, leaking sewers and shortages of potable water are acute problems in African cities, and serious ones in many Latin American and Caribbean cities.

Providing sufficient water is becoming increasingly difficult. Nearby surface and underground sources have already been exhausted in many cases, including Amman, Delhi, Santiago and Mexico City, which are forced to pump water from increasing distances and up increasing heights. Half of all cities in Asia experience water shortages on a daily basis.

Cities, as well as being places of opportunity, centres of political power and drivers of economic prosperity, can also be the refuge of those displaced by war or economic deprivation, and in much of the developing world include large slum areas where infrastructure is minimal. In the shanty towns (known locally as favelas, bustees and bidonvilles) that typically house 30 per cent of city inhabitants, rising to 60 per cent in Africa, overall deprivations are exemplified by lack of access to water and sanitation. All municipalities understand that infectious disease spreads much faster and more lethally in crowded settlements.

Considerable efforts were made to upgrade water and sanitation services to meet the Millennium Development Goals. Some countries, including China, Brazil, India, Morocco and Tunisia, implemented large-scale slum upgrading programmes and invested heavily in water and sanitation services. In many cases, the costs of conventional water-borne sewerage outside the elite town centre and suburbs mean that septic tanks and other single unit systems are the only option.

The positive picture conveyed by high tallies of urban service coverage can therefore be misleading. Recent surveys in poor urban neighbourhoods have found that water and sanitation coverage is significantly worse than reported, due to over-use of communal taps and toilet blocks.

According to UN-Habitat, sanitation is one of the three least developed components of urban infrastructure in developing world cities generally (the others are transportation and recreation). The inadequate provision of services to create a healthy and pleasant living environment has serious implications for urban prosperity, and for the fulfilment to citizens of the city's promise of a 'better life'.

INCREASING URBAN POPULATIONS
1990, 2000, 2010

10 million urban dwellers

10 million slum dwellers

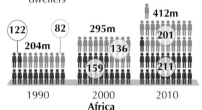

Africa

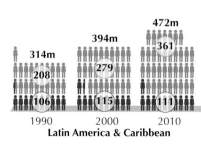

Latin America & Caribbean

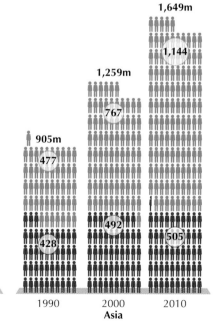

Asia

◄ *14 Water for Sanitation*

Reinforced pipes being laid
for the Cutzamala project.

MEXICO CITY'S WATER CRISIS

Mexico City, built on the site of a drained lake and prone to flooding, struggles to supply its rapidly increasing population with drinking water, and to dispose of the city's wastewater safely.

All water and wastewater flow estimates are in cubic metres per second, rounded

MEXICO CITY
Total water supply **83**

but 40% 'lost' through leaks or illicit use

cost of pumping
water to city:

22p
per litre

Lerma river basin **5**

Cutzamala river basin **15**
150 km, rising 1,100 metres
7 dams and **reservoirs** for storage
6 major pumping stations
water purification plant

Other river and springs **3**

How water is used:

agricultural
15%
industrial
6%

**municipal
79%**

groundwater **60**

abstraction – recharge =
overdraft of (28)
contributing to ground subsidence
of **5–40 cm** a year

**How residents receive
water supply:**

88% piped water

12% water tanker
2% wells, streams
└ heavily polluted
└ in unplanned development of Iztapalapa,
1 tanker provides daily water supply to
1,800 people on average
└ 70% of city has <12 hours of running water
per day, and **18%** of residents have to wait
days for a few hours of piped water

Wastewater
The metropolitan area generates **40**
of wastewater, but has capacity for only **10**
The city's sewage system originally functioned
on gravity, but because of subsidence now
requires pumping. Only **8%** of wastewater is
treated. The new Eastern Discharge Tunnel will
be one of the largest of its kind in the world.

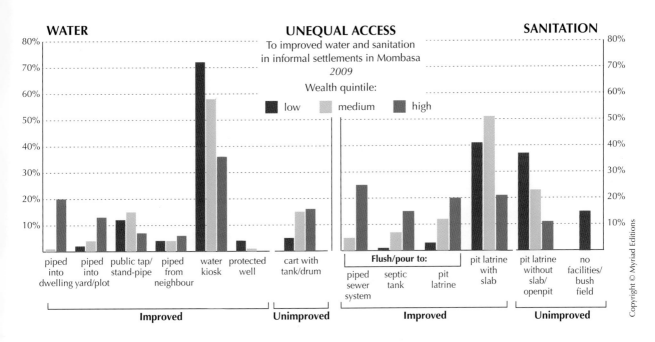

WATER

UNEQUAL ACCESS
To improved water and sanitation
in informal settlements in Mombasa
2009
Wealth quintile:
low   medium   high

SANITATION

piped into dwelling | piped into yard/plot | public tap/ stand-pipe | piped from neighbour | water kiosk | protected well | cart with tank/drum

Improved | **Unimproved**

Flush/pour to:
piped sewer system | septic tank | pit latrine | pit latrine with slab | pit latrine without slab/ openpit | no facilities/ bush field

Improved | **Unimproved**

16 WATER AT HOME

There are huge discrepancies in the amount of water people use in the home, depending on water availability and lifestyle.

In the industrialized world, where water is laid on by household connection, water for domestic purposes includes usage for laundry, cooking, washing-up and toilets, as well as for washing cars, sprinkling gardens, and filling swimming pools. Where people are still living at subsistence level, domestic water may be used for livestock, and productive activities such as growing vegetables.

Estimates of the amount of water actually used in rich-world homes vary widely, and range from 150 litres a person a day, to 800 litres in hot seasons or climates. As awareness of water stress has grown, steps have been taken to reduce water use. Service providers apply price-control mechanisms, such as metering and charging higher unit prices. Toilets, showers and washing-machines are nowadays designed to be water-conserving.

In parts of the world where water for the home has to be carried from a stream, pump or tap, at further distance in the dry season, or where its purchase represents a major expense, water is used very sparingly – no more than 15 or 20 litres a day. This may mean that insufficient water is devoted to effective personal hygiene.

Although the link between water and ill-health is usually associated with drinking-water contamination, a plentiful supply of water via a household tap is more important in preventing transmission of disease. A safe drinking water supply reduces diarrhoeal disease by 6 per cent; while improved hygiene, especially washing hands with soap, can reduce diarrhoeal incidence by as much as 40 per cent.

Initiatives to ensure a cheap and accessible supply of water to people's homes are therefore vital, as are those that build awareness about hygiene. Those planning household water services also need to understand that supplies need to be sufficient for a wide variety of purposes related to family survival, depending on the local economy and culture.

Litres of water
used daily
in and around
the home
in 2010:

USA

333

Rwanda
11

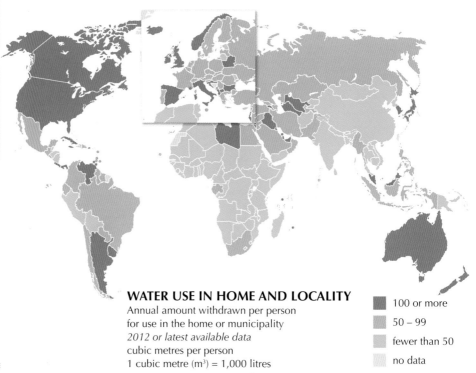

WATER USE IN HOME AND LOCALITY
Annual amount withdrawn per person
for use in the home or municipality
2012 or latest available data
cubic metres per person
1 cubic metre (m³) = 1,000 litres

- 100 or more
- 50 – 99
- fewer than 50
- no data

54

Alaska

Hawaii

Washington
Oregon
Idaho
Montana
North Dakota
Minnesota
Michigan
Vermont
Maine
New Hampshire
Mass.
New York
R. I.
Connecticut
Nevada
Utah
Wyoming
South Dakota
Wisconsin
Iowa
Penn.
Maryland
New Jersey
Delaware
California
Colorado
Nebraska
Illinois
Indiana
Ohio
West Virginia
Virginia
D.C.
Kansas
Missouri
Kentucky
North Carolina
Arizona
New Mexico
Oklahoma
Arkansas
Tennessee
South Carolina
Alabama
Georgia
Mississippi
Texas
Louisiana
Florida

US RESIDENTIAL WATER USE

Daily amount per person
used indoors and outdoors
2010
gallons per day

- 125 or more
- 75 – 124
- fewer than 75

2005: 98 gallons

2010: 88 gallons

DECLINING USE

Average US residential water use

WATER IN THE HOME

Typical patterns of consumption
in an industrialized country
2012

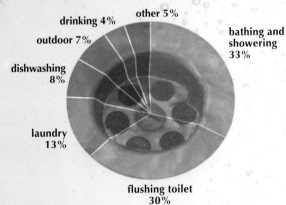

drinking 4%

other 5%

outdoor 7%

bathing and showering 33%

dishwashing 8%

laundry 13%

flushing toilet 30%

THE TRUE COST OF WATER

**A wasteful showerhead
can lead to an annual loss to the
average US family of:**

2,900 gallons

(11,000 litres)
of water

+

enough energy to power their

home for **13 days**

=

$70 per year

17 WATER AND DISEASE

Water's critical role in hygiene and sanitation, and in the spread of diarrhoeal disease, confers on it a central place in public health.

Many diseases labelled "water-related" should more accurately be described as sanitation- or hygiene-related. The diarrhoeal diseases – such as cholera, typhoid and dysentery – are classic examples of infections transmitted by failure to maintain a barrier between humans and faecal matter, and the consequent presence of bacteria on hands after visiting the toilet, which enter the body by the "faecal–oral" route.

Studies of handwashing habits reveal that fewer than 20 per cent of people wash their hands with soap after defecation. Diarrhoea is responsible for an estimated 840,000 deaths a year, many of them young children, and hand-washing alone reduces the risk of contracting diarrhoea by 23 to 40 per cent. The problem is that people who have to carry their water long distances are naturally sparing in their use of this precious resource in the home.

Other diseases that can be reduced by more stringent hygiene practices include skin and eye infections such as scabies and trachoma. Intestinal parasitic worms are transmitted by contact with infected faeces, often by children running about barefoot. Such non-life-threatening conditions of poor hygiene interconnect with undernutrition, subnormal energy and slow childhood development. Diseases of poor sanitation are therefore invariably diseases of poverty and ignorance.

DEATHS FROM DIARRHOEA

Attributable to inadequate water, and inadequate sanitation and handwashing
2012
low- and middle-income countries

● number

DECLINING DEATHS FROM DIARRHOEA

As a percentage of total deaths among children aged <5 years
2000 & 2013

2000　　2003

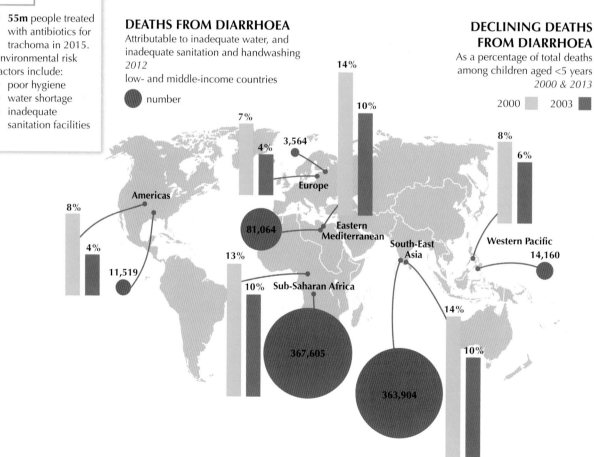

Many diseases are indirectly connected to water, because vectors that transmit them breed in rivers, ponds and other water sources, or they are contracted by imbibing the infective agent, such as guinea-worm (now nearly eradicated).

Of infections associated with standing water, malaria is the best-known and most deadly, with 214 million cases annually, and nearly half a million deaths every year, 90 per cent of them in Africa. The mosquitoes that carry the malarial parasite, which they transmit to humans when sucking their blood, breed in standing water, and attempts to eradicate the insects with insecticides, or to reduce their opportunities to breed, have largely failed. Encouragingly, there has been a major reduction in malaria deaths in recent years, mostly by the use of insecticide-treated bed-nets, which protect people while they sleep.

Other diseases carried by the mosquito include the Zika virus, whose rapid spread across South America prompted the WHO to declare a Public Health Emergency in 2016. Dengue also enters the body via the mosquito's bite. This viral disease has spread around the world in recent years and causes 960 million infections annually.

Other neglected tropical diseases affect people living without adequate water sources or sanitation, and in close proximity to live-stock, mainly in Africa. These include 120 million cases a year of onchocerciasis (river blindness) transmitted by blackfly; and 240 million cases of schistosomiasis (bilharzia), transmitted via water snails.

40%
of the world's population is at risk from dengue

MALARIA
Number of confirmed and presumed cases by WHO region
2013

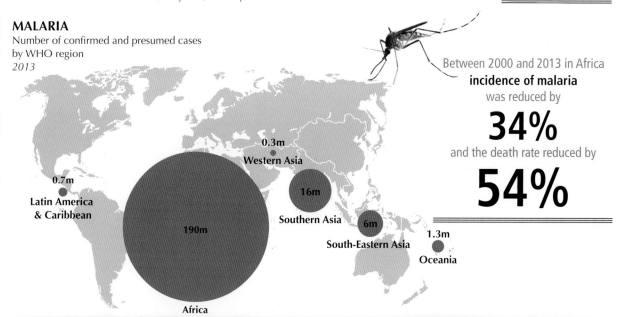

Between 2000 and 2013 in Africa
incidence of malaria
was reduced by

34%
and the death rate reduced by

54%

0.3m
Western Asia

0.7m
Latin America & Caribbean

190m

16m

Southern Asia

6m
South-Eastern Asia

1.3m
Oceania

Africa

BLIGHTED LIVES

Onchocerciasis
- Caused by a filarial worm *Onchocerca volvulus*, transmitted to humans through black flies, which breed in fast-flowing water.
- **120m** people are at risk, most of whom live in tropical Africa.
- In 2013, **100m** anti-bacterial treatments were distributed in 24 affected countries there.

Schistosomiasis
- Contracted by infection with parasitic blood flukes carried by water snails.
- Causes chronic ill-health, reducing people's capacity to learn or to work.
- Can be treated with chemotherapy.
- In 2012–13:
  700m people at risk, **249m** people affected, **42m** treated

PART 4 WATER FOR ECONOMIC PRODUCTION

Water plays a central part in all economic productivity, either directly as an input, or as part of the process or context in which economic activity takes place. That industry and manufacturing require large volumes of water is now given more recognition, and the need for water-conserving technologies is better appreciated.

Water's most obvious direct contribution to the global economy is through agriculture. Four-fifths of the world's cropland can manage with rain, but the rest needs irrigation from rivers or aquifers, either to multiply seasonal harvests or yields, or to make the desert bloom. The burst of industrial-scale impoundments and irrigation networks that took place during the second half of the 20th century has now slowed. Small-scale irrigation, which is less expensive and environmentally disruptive, now commands more attention, as does more efficient use of moisture in the soil and expansion of "green" water yields.

Agriculture still absorbs the lion's share of water for economic production – accounting for 70 per cent of extractions globally – but industrial usage is rising. In high-income countries, the proportion already amounts to 60 per cent. Concerns over water use in industry focus both on volumes extracted, and – more importantly – on discharges of polluted effluent. Certain industries use more water than others, the paper and metal industries in particular. The fuel industry also requires water, for powering turbines to generate electricity, as a cooling agent in power stations, and to grow biofuels.

Aquaculture has rapidly expanded in recent years, alongside the decline in wild freshwater fish stocks. Migratory fish and other organisms essential to support the aquatic ecosystem are not able to pass dams, and the fragmentation of rivers has therefore seriously affected traditional fishing livelihoods. However, the growth of commercial fish farming, especially in Asia, has opened up new employment opportunities as well as contributing to the global food system. Most of this produce is exported to industrialized countries to satisfy their demand for fish and seafood. But pollution, coastal degradation and lack of regulation have imposed considerable environmental costs.

Economic activity around the consumption of water by human beings for drinking and domestic use has also increased in recent years. Widespread privatization of water utilities has raised the price of municipal and domestic supplies, especially for the poor, and whether profits should be made out of trade in such an essential, life-giving substance remains controversial. Meanwhile, the bottled water industry has hugely expanded. Once again, the environmental costs of the industry are heavy, and questions as to whether the product is really superior to water from the tap have caused a degree of backlash.

18 WATER FOOTPRINT

CONTRASTING WATER FOOTPRINTS

Proportion embedded from national and external sources

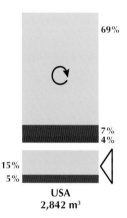

○↻ national source

◁ external source

▢ agriculture

■ industry

▨ domestic

69%

7%
4%

15%
5%

USA
2,842 m³

24%
0.5%
1%

64%

11%

UK
1,258 m³

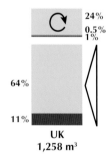

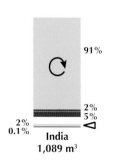

91%

2%
5%

2%
0.1%

India
1,089 m³

Industrialized lifestyles consume water embedded in imported foodstuffs and manufactured items. This hidden or "virtual" water, or water that has been used and polluted in a production process, is known as its "water footprint".

The concept helps point to how individuals, societies, or governments can most sensibly conserve water and use it economically. The water footprint can be measured for a single process, such as growing rice, the manufacture of a product such as a car or book, or for a multinational company or country. Measurement can be by volume, monetary value or other functional unit.

The footprint has three components, based on the source of the water: rainfall or moistened soil (green), rivers, lakes or aquifers (blue), and the volume of water required to dilute pollutants, such as industrial waste or agro-chemical run-off, and regain freshwater safety.

An assessment of water consumption that includes embedded water gives a different view from one where these are omitted. It includes the water in imports, while exports containing embedded water are deducted. For example, the USA's water footprint is mostly from its own vast sources, but 20 per cent is imported, the largest contribution coming from China's Yangtze Basin.

Countries that are heavy importers have externalized their water footprints: 77 per cent of the UK's footprint, for example, lies outside its borders. Where items are produced in water-short areas and exported to water-abundant ones, this represents a skewing of the use of water resources that is not conducive to sound water management or conservation on a global basis.

Several factors contribute to a large water footprint. Food production in a hot climate in which moisture rapidly evaporates from the soil requires proportionately more water than in a temperate one, accounting for the large footprints of some tropical countries. Inefficient use of water, including leakage and pollution, also enlarges the overall footprint.

60

◄ 13 Water for Food

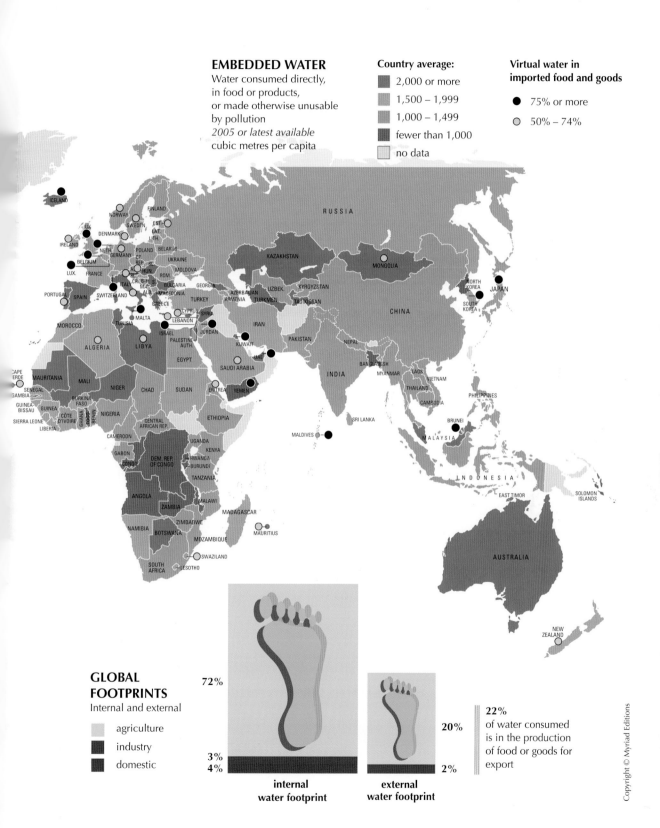

EMBEDDED WATER

Water consumed directly, in food or products, or made otherwise unusable by pollution
2005 or latest available
cubic metres per capita

Country average:

- 2,000 or more
- 1,500 – 1,999
- 1,000 – 1,499
- fewer than 1,000
- no data

Virtual water in imported food and goods

- ● 75% or more
- ○ 50% – 74%

GLOBAL FOOTPRINTS

Internal and external

- agriculture
- industry
- domestic

internal water footprint
- 72%
- 3%
- 4%

external water footprint
- 20%
- 2%

22% of water consumed is in the production of food or goods for export

19 WATER FOR IRRIGATION

20%
of cropland
is irrigated

A fifth of the world's cropland cannot support agriculture purely on water falling as rain – "green" water. So farmers use "blue" water (surface or groundwater), channelled from rivers, streams and lakes or pumped from aquifers, to cultivate crops in rain-short areas or dry seasons.

In arid and monsoonal areas, hydraulic systems of irrigation have been in use since time immemorial. Traditional lifting systems for paddy-fields and canals, check-dams that captured seasonal flows, and other water-manipulation devices aided the development of year-round agriculture. Many such technologies are still used today.

In the early 20th century, irrigation on an industrial scale took off in the USA. Mega-dams then spread worldwide, notably to Asia, where high-yielding "green revolution" hybrid crop strains rely heavily on irrigation. Despite controversy over costs and benefits, and opposition to their social and environmental damage, the large dams beloved of presidents and chief ministers are still being built in many regions. Water from aquifers has been similarly deployed for irrigation, often without restraint or recognition of non-renewable limits.

The area of irrigated land now amounts to nearly one-third of cultivated land. This makes a substantial contribution to the global food basket, producing 60 per cent of cereals in developing countries – an important source of calories. But the take-off of water for irrigation has been so extreme that some great rivers are reduced to a trickle. Basins have become effectively "closed" because the limits to water extraction have been reached, or breached.

Given that agriculture currently accounts for 70 per cent of "blue" water take-off, the constraint to further expansion of this kind is evident. Smaller-scale irrigation, cooperatively managed by farmers themselves, would now be a more productive and water-efficient way to proceed. Several of the vast irrigation projects attractive to centrally managed economies have led to severe waterlogging, soil salinity and water squandering.

Irrigation will continue to play an important part in agriculture, but expanded productivity from both irrigated and rain-fed areas, and techniques emphasizing water conservation, are now needed. One approach is to reduce water volume, allowing mild stress during plant growth at stages less sensitive to moisture deficiency. "Deficit irrigation" has been effective in China and Pakistan, bringing water savings for only modest yield reductions, and offering one route to a water-efficient future.

WATER WITHDRAWALS FOR IRRIGATION

Total per year
2010
million cubic metres

- 12,000 – 32,000
- 1,000 – 9,999
- fewer than 1,000

Reliance on groundwater:

🌐 groundwater withdrawn for irrigation is 85% or more of total

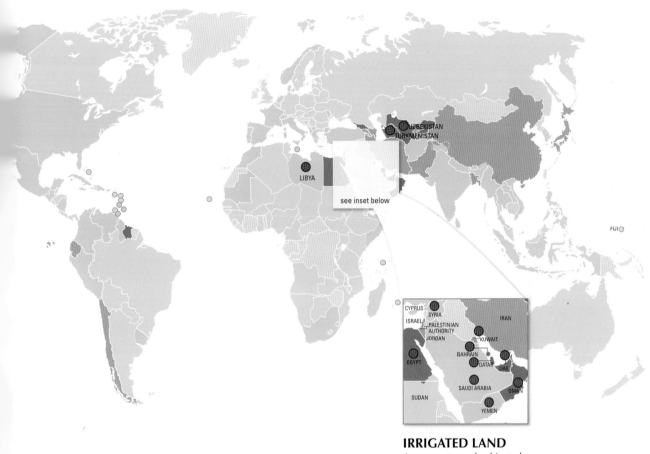

CYPRUS
SYRIA
ISRAEL
PALESTINIAN
AUTHORITY
JORDAN
KUWAIT
BAHRAIN
QATAR
UAE
EGYPT
SAUDI ARABIA
OMAN
SUDAN
YEMEN
IRAN

UZBEKISTAN
TURKMENISTAN
LIBYA
FIJI

see inset below

IRRIGATED LAND

As percentage of cultivated area
latest available 2000–14

- 75 % or more
- 50% – 74%
- 10% – 49%
- less than 10%
- no data

Water withdrawn for
agriculture as percentage of
renewable water resources

- ⬤ 85% or more

Deficit irrigation

Deficit irrigation involves reducing the amount of water given to a plant at certain stages of its cycle in a way that minimizes the impact on yield.

On the North China Plain a study of winter wheat reduced water use by 25% by using two irrigations instead of the usual four, but still achieved acceptably high yields, thereby maximizing net profits.

A project in the San Joaquin Valley, California, USA showed that the amount of water given to trees could be reduced by 50% in the three months post-harvest (the hottest time of the year, when water is at a premium) without any noticeable impact on the quality or quantity of fruit in the following year.

20 WATER FOR FISHERIES

Fish – in rivers, lakes and in saltwater coastal areas – make a major contribution to the global food supply, and are increasingly farmed as a cash crop. The average recent increase in fish consumption per head of global population is far higher than the increase in meat consumption.

Over 200 million people are dependent on fishing, with small-scale producers occupying pride of place, although illegal industrial-scale fishing threatens their livelihoods in parts of Africa and Asia. Fish is the primary source of protein for millions of people in the developing world. In Bangladesh, it provides up to 80 per cent of animal protein in the diet, and a similar picture prevails among many riverine and lake-side dwellers, whose fish catches are under-reported.

The volume of fish captured in the wild has remained more or less stagnant since the 1990s. Many marine fish stocks have suffered from over-fishing, and freshwater stocks have also fallen dramatically, largely due to river fragmentation. Migratory fish, such as salmon, cannot pass dams, and changes in river flow affect all aquatic organisms. One fifth of freshwater species are classified as extinct, endangered or vulnerable.

The volume of fish produced by aquaculture, has been rising steadily, in terms of volume and, to an even greater degree, of value. Most of the expansion has occurred in Asia, now the centre of both aquaculture and the production of aquatic plants for consumption.

In the industrialized world, demand for fish and seafood has exploded, especially for imported Asian fish, projected to be responsible for 70 per cent of consumption by 2030. As a result, the greatest recent growth is in large farms raising high-value predatory fish such as salmon, tuna and shrimp. These require feeding on smaller species such as anchovy and herring, which are being over-fished from the oceans for this purpose. Aquaculture now provides nearly half of the fish consumed annually. China is the world's largest producer.

The impact of fish farming on the environment has been profound. More than half of Asia's mangroves have been lost or degraded by their development. Poorly managed farms can be environmentally devastating, creating dead zones on lake or sea floor full of excess feed and effluent.

Properly guided, the growth in fish farming is a hopeful trend for the world food basket, as long as attention is given to sustainability and standards. These are not confined to aquatic and environmental. Slavery has been discovered on Thai fishing vessels.

FISH CONSUMED
Weight per person
1960 & 2012

10kg

1960

19kg

2012

Threat to local economy

Up to a quarter of jobs in West Africa are linked to fisheries, but each year illegal industrial-scale fishing boats harvest $1.3 billion worth of fish from its waters. Greenpeace recently reported 114 cases of illegal fishing by Chinese-flagged boats operating in the region's coastal waters.

RATE OF CHANGE
Annual percentage growth rate
by region
2005–10

capture ▮ aquaculture ▯

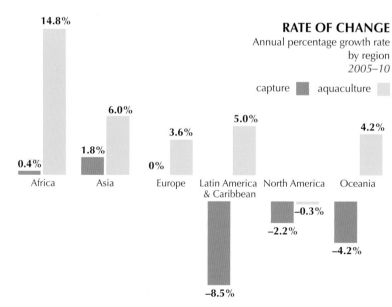

14.8%
6.0%
1.8%
0.4%
Africa   Asia

3.6%
0%
Europe

5.0%
−8.5%
Latin America & Caribbean

−0.3%
−2.2%
North America

4.2%
−4.2%
Oceania

AQUACULTURE
Production of fish, crustaceans and molluscs
2013
tonnes

- ■ 43.5 million
- ■ 1 – 4.5 million
- ■ 100,000 – 999,999
- 10,000 – 99,999
- under 10,000
- no data

Aquatic plants produced by aquaculture:

- 13.5m tonnes
- 9.3m tonnes
- 1m–1.5m tonnes

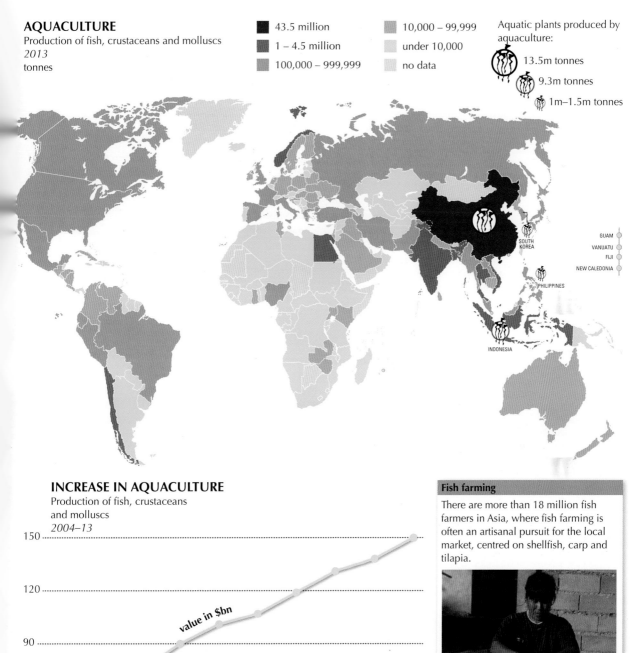

GUAM
VANUATU
FIJI
NEW CALEDONIA
SOUTH KOREA
PHILIPPINES
INDONESIA

INCREASE IN AQUACULTURE
Production of fish, crustaceans and molluscs
2004–13

value in $bn

weight in tonnes

150
120
90
60
30

2004 2005 2006 2007 2008 2009 2010 2011 2012 2013

Fish farming

There are more than 18 million fish farmers in Asia, where fish farming is often an artisanal pursuit for the local market, centred on shellfish, carp and tilapia.

21 WATER FOR INDUSTRY

Just over 19 per cent of all freshwater withdrawn worldwide is used by industry, but in high-income countries this proportion rises to over 50 per cent.

More than half of this water is used either for generating electricity, or for cooling power stations, and is returned to its source virtually unchanged. Other major industrial uses of water – including chemical and petroleum plants, metal industries, the wood, pulp and paper industry, food processing and machinery manufacture – are much heavier polluters.

Industrial water use has increased only slowly since the 1980s as a result of concerted efforts to control its use and treatment. However, as more developing countries industrialize, the global industrial use of water is expected to rise steeply over the next 25 years, with implications for water pollution. In developing countries, 70 per cent of industrial waste is dumped untreated into rivers. Indiscriminate industrial discharges have also contaminated soils and underground aquifers.

The amount of water used in the production of industrial products varies widely. Heavy users of water include the paper and metal industries, and the electronics industry, which requires high-quality, treated water. Biofuels, whose production has recently soared, need much more water to produce than do oil-based fuels. The financial value generated by the use of water in industrial processes is generally greater than that from agriculture, but it also varies widely between countries.

Multinational companies operating in water-stressed areas are already applying water-conservation measures. But small- and medium-sized enterprises have fewer means to meet water challenges in similar ways.

Balancing the demands of sustainability against conventional ideas governing mass production is going to require changing paradigms. Water use is central to the dilemmas involved in spreading the benefits of industrialization equitably worldwide, without compromising environmental health. Many companies prefer to pay fines for pollution rather than invest in water treatment and conservation.

Global water demand for manufacturing is predicted to increase by

400%

2000–50

WATER FOR FUEL

Litres of water used to produce fuel sufficient to power a small car for one mile
2010

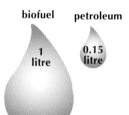

biofuel — 1 litre

petroleum — 0.15 litre

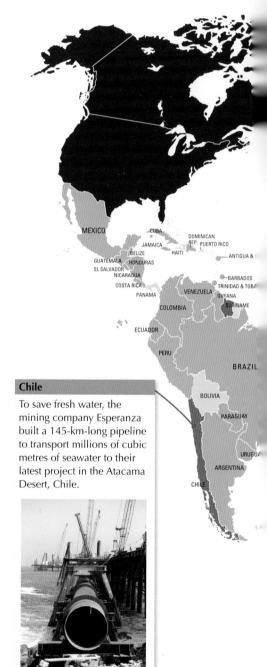

MEXICO, CUBA, JAMAICA, DOMINICAN REP., PUERTO RICO, BELIZE, HAITI, ANTIGUA &, GUATEMALA, HONDURAS, EL SALVADOR, NICARAGUA, BARBADOS, COSTA RICA, TRINIDAD & TOBA, VENEZUELA, GUYANA, PANAMA, SURINAME, COLOMBIA, ECUADOR, PERU, BRAZIL, BOLIVIA, PARAGUAY, URUGUA, ARGENTINA, CHILE

Chile

To save fresh water, the mining company Esperanza built a 145-km-long pipeline to transport millions of cubic metres of seawater to their latest project in the Atacama Desert, Chile.

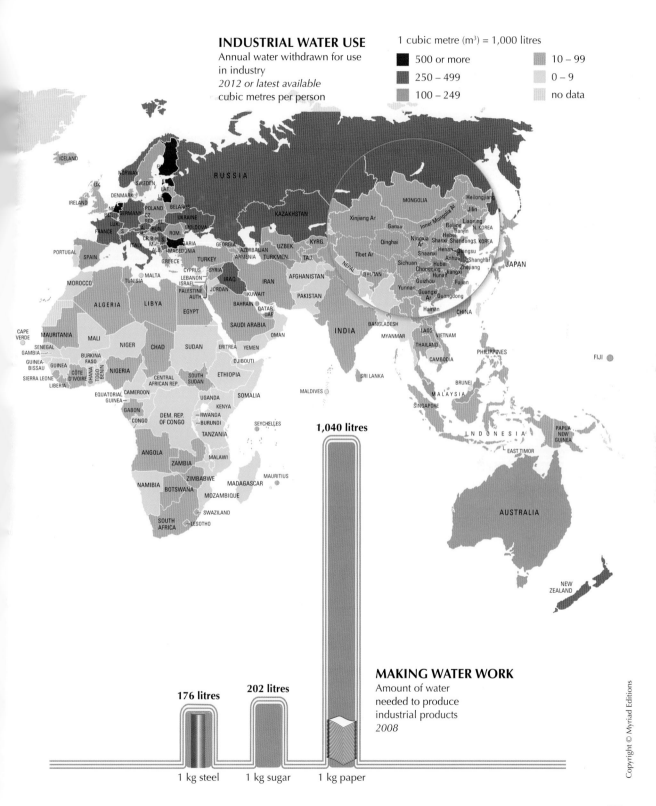

INDUSTRIAL WATER USE

Annual water withdrawn for use in industry
2012 or latest available
cubic metres per person

1 cubic metre (m³) = 1,000 litres

- 500 or more
- 250 – 499
- 100 – 249
- 10 – 99
- 0 – 9
- no data

MAKING WATER WORK

Amount of water needed to produce industrial products
2008

176 litres — 1 kg steel

202 litres — 1 kg sugar

1,040 litres — 1 kg paper

22 WATER FOR ENERGY

An increase
in electricity
generation of

70%

by 2035

translates into an
increase of

20%

in freshwater
withdrawals

GLOBAL ELECTRICITY GENERATION

By fuel
2013

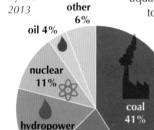

other 6%

oil 4%

nuclear 11%

hydropower 16%

coal 41%

natural gas 22%

Water plays a vital role in thermal power generation, which currently accounts for 80 per cent of global electricity production. The force of its flow is used to power turbines, and water also acts as a coolant in gas, coal and nuclear power stations.

Hydropower, which harnesses the force of water directly, accounts for 15 per cent of global electricity production. After a downturn in the 1990s, investment in hydropower infrastructure recently began to rise, on the basis that hydropower is a renewable, environmentally friendly form of power generation, as compared to coal-fired or nuclear power stations. The need to expand hydropower is used as a justification for the construction of large dams, in China, Africa and elsewhere.

The true costs of hydropower are frequently underestimated. The damage to fisheries and aquatic ecosystems may be inadequately factored in, and reduced river flows due to other factors, including climate change, may seriously affect output. Reservoirs behind large dams release greenhouse gases, and can also lead to high levels of evaporation and consequent water-use inefficiency.

Many dams built primarily for hydroelectricity generation – such as the Tucurui dam in Brazil and the Pak Mun in Thailand – have failed to do so cost-effectively. The Grand Ethiopia Renaissance Dam (GERD) on the Blue Nile, on which work started in 2013, will only be able to use its total turbine capacity for between two and three months a year, when the river is at full flow.

An increased demand for electricity, including from the 1.3 billion people who currently have no source of power, will translate into an increasing demand for water, given that 90 per cent of thermal energy production is water-intensive. Thus, high-efficiency power plants with more sophisticated cooling systems will be needed.

Harnessing fast natural river flows for power generation, or building small hydropower (SHP) schemes in remote rural areas, have many positive benefits that avoid the high costs and social and environmental problems associated with large dams. Where water is scarce, some of the electricity generated can be used to pump water into storage tanks for drinking or irrigation water. China has successfully used SHP technology to benefit over 300 million rural people. Worldwide, however, such schemes currently produce only a tenth of the power generated by large-scale plants.

Although **thermo-electric** power accounted for **45% of all water withdrawals** in the USA in 2010, it required **18% less fresh water** than in 2005, due partly to a switch to gas generation and to plants that **recirculate** the cooling water.

THERMO-ELECTRIC POWER

Freshwater withdrawals
by US state
2010
thousand cubic metres per day

- 30,000 or more
- 10,000 – 29,999
- 1,000 – 9,999
- less than 1,000

HYDROPOWER

As a percentage of
total electricity produced
2013 or latest available data

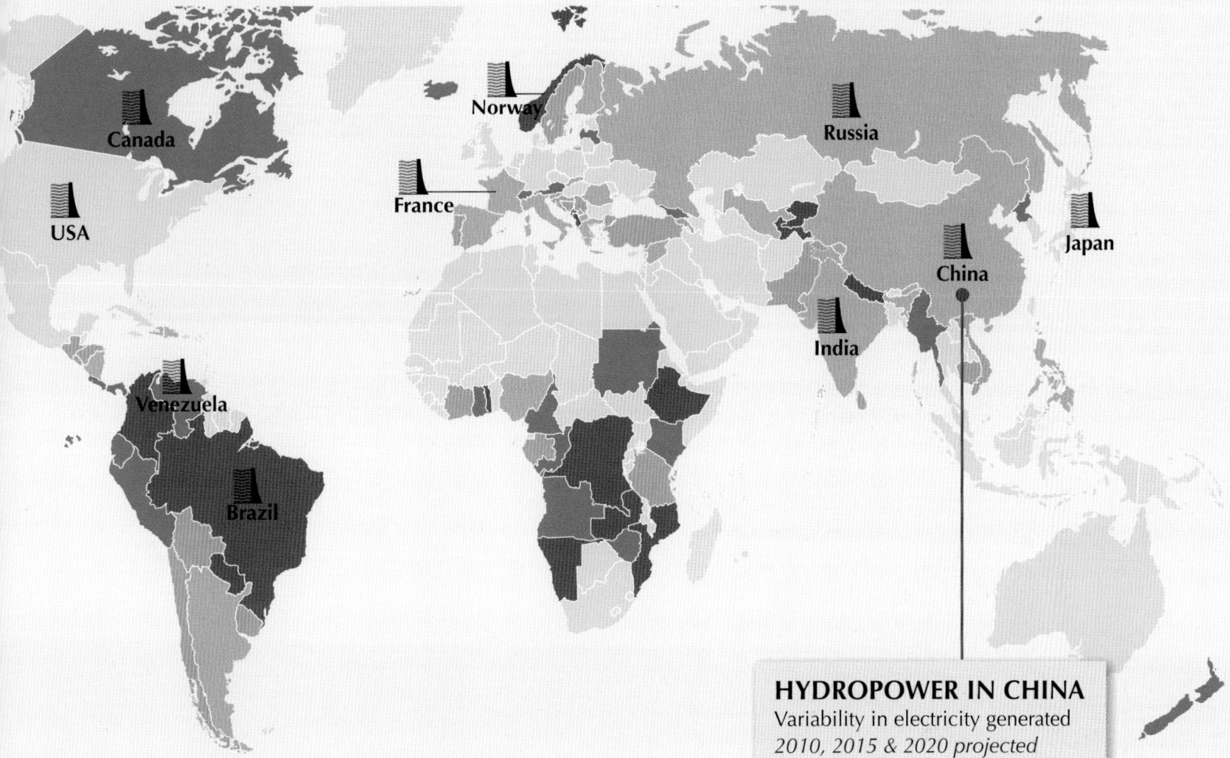

- 75% or more
- 50% – 74%
- 25% – 49%
- 10% – 24%
- less than 10%
- no data

75 million megawatthours or more
per year
1 megawatthour = power required to run a
single-bar electric fire for 1,000 hours

Canada

Norway

Russia

USA

France

Japan

Venezuela

China

India

Brazil

HYDROPOWER IN CHINA

Variability in electricity generated
2010, 2015 & 2020 projected
terrawatthours

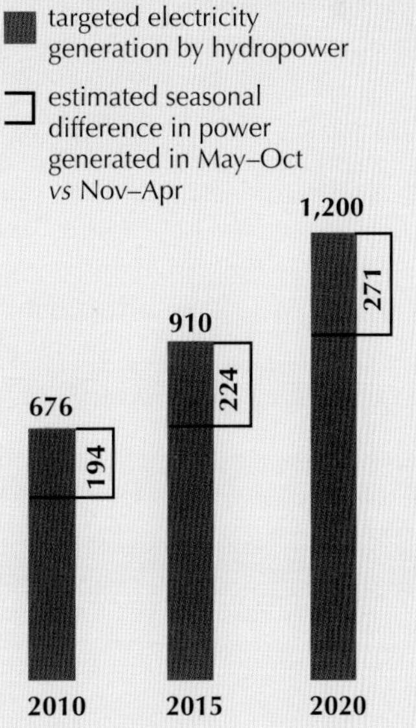

- targeted electricity
  generation by hydropower

- estimated seasonal
  difference in power
  generated in May–Oct
  vs Nov–Apr

	2010	2015	2020
targeted	676	910	1,200
seasonal	194	224	271

GROWTH OF HYDROPOWER

Regional shares
1973 & 2013

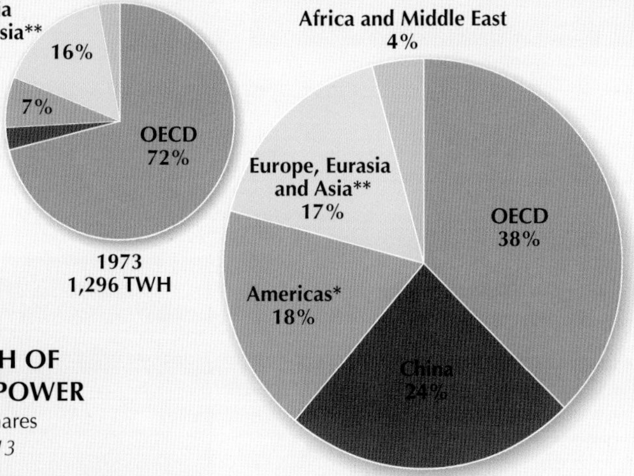

* excluding OECD countries
** excluding OECD countries and China

1973
1,296 TWH

- Africa and Middle East 3%
- Europe, Eurasia and Asia** 16%
- Americas* 7%
- China 3%
- OECD 72%

2013
3,874 TWH

- Africa and Middle East 4%
- Europe, Eurasia and Asia** 17%
- Americas* 18%
- China 24%
- OECD 38%

23 TRANSPORT AND LEISURE

Golf courses
in the USA
use about

2,080

**million gallons
(8,000m litres)**
of water a year

Water is integral to many productive and cultural activities not easily traceable in economic statistics. Seas and oceans, as well as beaches and coastal resorts, may predominate in both transport and leisure, but fresh water plays an important part.

For centuries, rivers were more important than roads as thoroughfares and communications networks. In prehistoric times, amber was brought by inland waterways from the Baltic to southern Europe, and the Egyptians solved the problem of navigation through rapids by building a canal to bypass a cataract on the Nile as early as 2300 BC.

The Chinese completed their 1,794-km Grand Canal in 609. Construction of Amsterdam's main canals started in 1613. The modern age of European canal transport dates from 1681, when the Canal du Midi joined the Bay of Biscay to the Mediterranean. In the UK, 4,000 miles of canals were constructed before the advent of the railways that over time rendered them obsolete.

China, the USA and a few other countries still rely on navigable inland waterways for transporting freight, but elsewhere the income generated from rivers and canals comes mainly from pleasure craft. Water plays a major role in the tourist and leisure industry in several ways. Spa towns in Europe have a long history as destinations for the leisured classes. More recently, reservoirs and natural lakes have been used for sailing and water sports.

However, the heavy demand placed by golf courses on freshwater supplies is beginning to be questioned, especially where water resources are stressed. In drought-ridden California, some golf club managers are tearing out their grass, planting drought-resistant vegetation, and promoting the idea that "brown is the new green".

Great Lakes

115 million tonnes of US freight was carried between the Great Lakes in 2012, the bulk of which was iron ore, coal and building materials.

Mississippi

**domestic
256m**

**inbound
69m**

**foreign
outbound
122m**

**Total freight
in 2012:
447m tonnes**

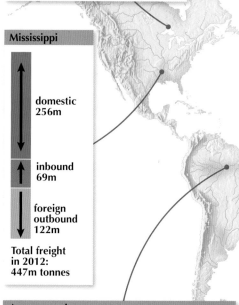

Amazon cruises

Traditional riverboats, or more overtly modern cruise ships, are part of the region's growing tourist trade and, if not regulated, are likely to have a major impact on the river's ecosystem.

WATERBORNE FREIGHT IN USA

On inland waterways
2012

Total: 564 million tonnes

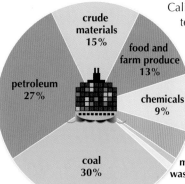

crude materials 15%

food and farm produce 13%

petroleum 27%

chemicals 9%

manufactured goods 5%

manufactured equipment 1%

waste and scrap <1%

coal 30%

◀ 10 Droughts

European waterways

Several of Europe's largest rivers are still used to transport freight, but most of the canal networks vital to the Industrial Revolution are now almost entirely used for recreation.

Artificial beaches

In an attempt to generate more income from their rivers, several city authorities have created artificial beaches. The first was on the Seine, in Paris in 2000, but it has been imitated in London and other European cities.

China's waterways

China's 125,900 km of navigable rivers and canals are used to transport an increasing amount of freight.

2002 1.4bn tonnes

2007 2.8bn tonnes

2012 5.6bn tonnes

Kerala backwaters

These 900 km of interconnected lakes and canals have for centuries been used to transport goods and people, but are now being used to generate income from tourism.

Nile

The Nile has been used for millennia to transport goods locally, but its variable flow, many dams, and political instability make bulk, long-distance waterborne transport impossible.

Golf courses

The use of water to maintain golf courses is a hotly contested issue. Keeping a course of 100 or so acres of turf healthy in a dry climate may require as much as 130,000 gallons (492,000 litres) a day.

In drought-affected California, where drought restrictions were implemented in 2015, golf course managers are incorporating water-saving technologies, such as rainwater harvesting, recycling of water, the use of more drought-resistant grasses, and simply digging up the turf on the fairway margins.

24 WATER FOR SALE

In developing countries, the poorest households may spend up to

11%
of their income
on water

PRICE OF PIPED WATER
and wastewater disposal as percentage of average net disposable income
2008
selected industrialized countries

Poland
1.4%

Germany
0.9%

UK, France
0.7%

Australia
0.6%

Spain
0.5%

Japan
0.3%

USA, Canada
0.3%

Norway, Sweden
0.3%

South Korea
0.3%

Mexico
0.2%

Italy
0.2%

The sale of water is an inevitable part of any organized delivery system, whether by haulers and carters, or by the most sophisticated pipeline and pump-house operation.

"God provided the water, but not the pipes", is the industry's way of pointing out that if water is to be laid on to homes, shops and offices, equipment and engineering are needed, and the water it delivers has to be paid for. However, what the price should be to different customers – farmer, industrialist, householder, villager or slum-dweller – and who, if anyone, should benefit from its sale, remain open to debate.

People living in the countryside traditionally collected their water from streams and rivers or drew it from dug wells. Water was seen as a free natural resource and its common ownership was the basis of water laws stretching back into antiquity. But water has also been sold for domestic consumption since time immemorial, by water carriers, carters and vendors, who collect it, transport and sell it by the containerful, using a five-gallon plastic can or whatever is locally standard. This trade still survives in those corners of the world where piped water has yet to be laid on to every building.

So essential is an adequate supply of safe water to life and health that, following the industrial revolution in Europe and North America, the principle was accepted that – while customers paid water rates – supplies should be subsidized. But in many parts of the developing world where water sources are under severe stress, utilities operating on this principle cannot serve expanding populations efficiently – or even at all.

Environmental awareness led to the recognition in the early 1990s that "water is an economic good" and was being wastefully managed and squandered. The subsequent deployment of market mechanisms to control the use of water has been controversial. The poor often have to pay the full market price, while the better-off and business or industrial users are subsidized. Despite recognition by the UN Assembly in 2012 that water costs should not exceed 3 per cent of household income, many of the poorest households in developing countries are forced to pay much more than that.

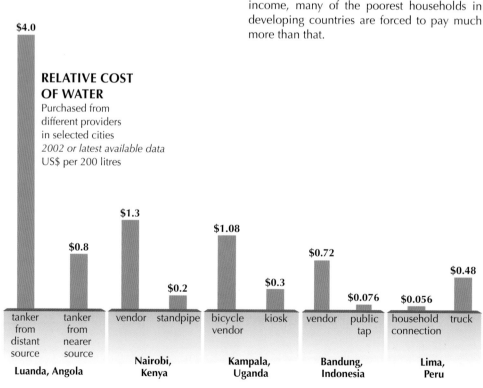

RELATIVE COST OF WATER
Purchased from different providers in selected cities
2002 or latest available data
US$ per 200 litres

	Luanda, Angola		Nairobi, Kenya		Kampala, Uganda		Bandung, Indonesia		Lima, Peru	
tanker from distant source	tanker from nearer source	vendor	standpipe	bicycle vendor	kiosk	vendor	public tap	household connection	truck
$4.0	$0.8	$1.3	$0.2	$1.08	$0.3	$0.72	$0.076	$0.056	$0.48

Bottled water has become ubiquitous. Globally, we now drink as much packaged water as we do milk – an average of 30 litres per person per year.

Bottled water's boom has been largely driven by fears about drinking-water quality. These may be legitimate in developing countries where the mains supply is not safe, but that is not the case in most industrialized countries. Nonetheless, companies such as Nestlé, Danone, Coca-Cola and Pepsi have managed to bottle a natural resource, capitalize on its supposed health-preserving properties, and market it successfully.

There has been a degree of backlash in countries where tap water is reliably potable, including a growing number of city, town and district councils in North America and the UK that have banned the spending of public money on bottled water. Some people are still prepared to spend up to a thousand times more on bottled water and have faith in its superior taste and safety. Blind tastings reveal, however, that many people cannot distinguish between bottled and tap water. This is not entirely surprising, since some bottled waters originate from the municipal water system – up to 45 per cent in the USA. Bottled water may not be as rigorously tested as that from the tap, and there have been several incidents of contamination.

In many countries, however, water sold in bottles or sachets represents, for those who can afford it, a safer alternative to water delivered by tanker or cart – or even to the piped supply – and the market is growing.

Water extraction for bottling can adversely affect groundwater availability for local farmers. After a landmark case in Kerala, India, Coca-Cola was forced to close down a bottling plant in 2004 because it had over-drawn and contaminated water supplies.

The energy involved in producing, packaging, transporting and cooling bottled water is immense. Some spring waters are transported far from their source. In the UK, for example, 22 per cent of bottled water is sourced overseas, some from as far away as the Himalayas. The discarded plastic and glass waste from bottled water also takes a huge toll on the environment around the globe, although manufacturers are generally increasing the PET content of their bottles, enabling more of them to be recycled.

Estimated energy to produce, package transport and cool bottled water:

2000
times
that of producing tap water

US annual consumption of bottled water in 2014:

34
gallons
(129 litres)
per person

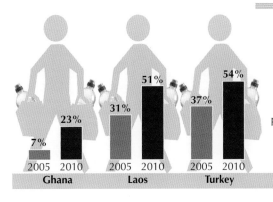

WATER IN BOTTLES OR SACHETS
Percentage of urban dwellers purchasing it as main drinking source
2005 & 2010

	Ghana		Laos		Turkey	
2005	7%		31%		37%	
2010		23%		51%		54%

TOP TEN MARKETS
For bottled water, by volume
2009 & 2014
billion litres

2014
2009

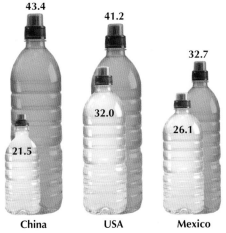
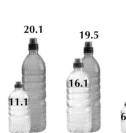

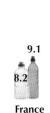
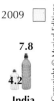

China	USA	Mexico	Indonesia	Brazil	Thailand	Italy	Germany	France	India
43.4 / 21.5	41.2 / 32.0	32.7 / 26.1	20.1 / 11.1	19.5 / 16.1	16.6 / 6.6	12.3 / 11.2	12.2 / 10.8	9.1 / 8.2	7.8 / 4.2

PART 5   DAMAGED WATER

The world's rivers and water bodies perform the function of natural drainage channels and sinks. Substances deposited on the land are washed into waterways by the rain, or gradually leach through the soil. This natural cleansing system absorbs waste matter and renders it harmless over time as long as it is not over-stretched.

The main problem today is that the volume of organic material discharged into rivers and streams is overwhelming their capacity to break it down, while other non-organic pollutants are even more toxic and cannot be absorbed. This damage to water is exacerbated by the fragmentation of rivers, which reduces their flow, increases turbidity and temperature, and helps reduce their life-sustaining capacity.

Human excreta is an important cause of water pollution. In the developing world, 90 per cent of sewage is discharged untreated into rivers, some of which are so laden with foul matter in the dry season that aquatic life is stifled. Since rivers continue to be used for bathing, laundry and even for drinking water in some places, the failure to treat pathogenic excreta before its discharge or to find other ways of confining it safely from human contact represents a major public health threat.

Rivers also receive industrial wastes, and in the developing world 70 per cent of these are similarly untreated. Some are organic, and eventually decompose, but not without absorbing oxygen and thereby depriving and depleting fish, plants and other aquatic creatures. Other contaminants, known as persistent organic pollutants (POPs), resist environmental degradation. Many originate from chemical fertilizers and pesticides, whose residues are washed into streams and may enter the food chain. These can build up in human tissues and have serious repercussions on health. Even more problematic are inorganic pollutants, such as heavy metals, and pharmaceutical residues that are not eliminated by conventional wastewater treatment.

Heavy industries and mines are the worst polluters of waterways. "Tailings ponds" that store toxic by-products may be accidentally spilled or overflow. Such risks are enhanced when vulnerable installations are situated near rivers or in earthquake zones. Disasters can cause serious damage to river ecosystems, killing fish and aquatic life for many miles downriver. Pollution loads in water courses are responsible for the extinction of many freshwater species, and chemical spillages have been known to contaminate the drinking water supplies of large downstream populations.

Controlling waste discharges at the source wherever possible, and regulating polluters by inflicting heavy penalties, is essential in an increasingly crowded and industrialized world. However expensive, effective management regimes to control pollution and prevent the destruction of aquatic life and water itself are essential for environmental health.

25 DAMMED RIVERS

66%

of the world's large river systems have become moderately or highly fragmented by dams

Nearly 60 per cent of the world's major rivers are impeded by large dams. Hydraulic engineering projects have impounded, stored and rechannelled the river waters in a monumental exercise to redesign natural flows.

Political leaders have always harnessed rivers to use their contents productively, for irrigation, storage, flood control, land reclamation and, more recently, hydropower. But however impressive ancient dams and "tanks" may have been, the hydraulic manipulation of rivers reached an entirely new, industrial scale in the 20th century.

Today, there are nearly 58,000 dams higher than 15 metres, of which 300 are over 150 metres and 20 over 250 metres. Sequences of large dams have the effect of fragmenting rivers, blocking their natural flow, and turning them into a series of artificial lakes, which dwindle to a trickle downstream.

The upstream effects of impounding water on such a scale include destruction of whole ecosystems and the species that depend on them. Human homes, settlements and historic sites are also submerged. Benefits gained may be short-lived. Inundated vegetation rots and releases methane – a greenhouse gas. Sediment, previously carried down the river, falls to the bottom as the water slows, substantially reducing the amount of water that can be held in reservoirs.

Downstream, the loss of the sediment diminishes floodplain fertility. Interrupted or reduced flows destroy wetlands and leave insufficient water for irrigation. Fisheries are also disrupted, with migrating species unable to pass up or downstream. River fragmentation is a major factor in the threat to a third of endangered freshwater fish species, and contributes significantly to pollution and water-quality degradation.

Greenhouse gas emissions

A conservative estimate is that 4% of all methane emissions are caused by the flow of water through large dams. Methane is produced by soil and vegetation that flows into and is produced in reservoirs. It has recently been discovered that not only are gases emitted at the water's surface, but in the spillways and turbines, and downstream, as the pressure on the water drops and dissolved methane is released.

Mississippi Delta

The damming and embankment of the river over many years has led to the silt it carries being deposited before it reaches the sea. The subsequent erosion of its delta makes New Orleans more vulnerable to flooding.

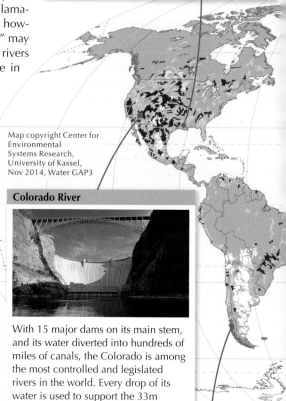

Map copyright Center for Environmental Systems Research, University of Kassel, Nov 2014, Water GAP3

Colorado River

With 15 major dams on its main stem, and its water diverted into hundreds of miles of canals, the Colorado is among the most controlled and legislated rivers in the world. Every drop of its water is used to support the 33m people living in its basin. Even though wastewater is returned to the river, the natural course of the river is normally completely dry for its last 150 km.

Hydropower in Patagonia

Thanks to a campaign to protect the ecology of Patagonia from the proposed five-dam HidroAysén project, in 2014 Chile's Committee of Ministers overturned the environmental permits previously issued for the project.

China

China has plans to build dams on the Lancang (Mekong), Nu (Salween), Yarlung Tsangpo (Brahmaputra), and the Jinsha. However, following a 2013 report by a coalition of Chinese NGOs, China's Ministry of Environmental Protection proposed an "ecological red line" protection system for rivers, proper assessments of the social impact of dams, and of their risks in areas of high seismic activity. On the Nu, work is now scheduled to start on only 5 of a proposed cascade of 13 dams.

ENVIRONMENTAL STRESS DUE TO FLOW ALTERATION
Deviation from natural flow regime
2014

- ■ severe
- ▨ medium
- ▨ high
- ▨ low

Indian dams

India has 4,300 large dams, submerging an area the size of Switzerland. Dozens more are planned, including a series in Arunachal Pradesh, harnessing the waters of the Brahmaputra and its tributaries. Critics point to the area's unstable geology, the variability in flow caused by climate change, and the fact that the local economy is unlikely to benefit from the additional power generated.

Meanwhile, China is also planning dams across tributaries in the same basin, with no indication that the two governments are coordinating management of this shared water.

Murray–Darling, Australia

The ecosystems of the Murray–Darling basin are under severe pressure due to unsustainable levels of extraction. The M–D Basin Authority has set limits on water use, buying water entitlements from irrigators, and investing in more efficient irrigation systems. Large purchases of water are used to increase flows and restore wetlands and vegetation.

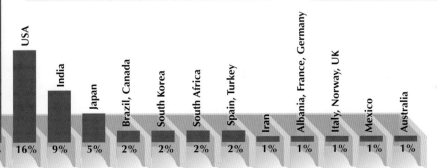

African Water Power

As part of a major infrastructure development programme (PIDA) agreed for Africa in 2012, 13 large dams are planned for power generation and irrigation. Large dams in Africa have a poor record in terms of cost-effectiveness, ecosystem damage, population displacement and performance. According to International Rivers, 11 projects indicate shortcomings, especially when located in unstable settings such as DR Congo.

WORLD DAMS
Percentage of total
2015

World total:
57,671

Country	%
China	41%
USA	16%
India	9%
Japan	5%
Brazil, Canada	2%
South Korea	2%
South Africa	2%
Spain, Turkey	2%
Iran	1%
Albania, France, Germany	1%
Italy, Norway, UK	1%
Mexico	1%
Australia	1%

26 DISPOSSESSION BY WATER

Up to

80
million

people have been dispossessed by dam-related submergence since 1950

Dams and disease

Slow-moving water in reservoirs and canals provides breeding grounds for disease-bearing organisms such as malarial mosquitoes and schistosomiasis-carrying snails.

A recent study found that 1.1 million malaria cases in Sub-Saharan Africa could be directly attributed to living within 5 km of a dam. Current planned dams in Africa are likely to add 56,000 cases annually.

Before the Diama dam on the Senegal river was built, there was no intestinal schistosomiasis, but afterwards prevalence rose to between 25% and 82%.

Lakes, rivers and beds of rivers exposed in the dry season are the basis of many people's livelihoods. Thus, man-made alterations in flows and water levels can destroy longstanding ways of life and sources of income.

Impounding water behind large dams and fragmenting rivers into artificial reservoirs has negative impacts on basin inhabitants. Most receive little or no compensation, and a disproportionate number belong to ethnic minorities. Many millions more people have their river-based livelihoods or health threatened, and those who suffer these consequences rarely benefit from dam outputs such as electricity or irrigation water.

China is the world's most prolific dam builder, having constructed 22,000 large dams in the past 60 years, many in densely populated areas. These have required the resettlement of over 23 million people – equivalent to the population of Australia. Over 8 million struggle to make a living as a result.

Large dams in India have also caused the forcible relocation of millions of people, many of them indigenous, whose rights are ignored with impunity. Corruption associated with these massive projects often extends to compensation allocations which, if paid at all, vanish into the wrong hands.

Although those relocated are often promised "land for land", sufficient good land is rarely available, so they are given cash instead. Once that is exhausted, they end up on the poverty scrapheap. Others find their livelihoods ruined by the ecological makeover wrought by the dam. Fisheries and forests are permanently affected, and traditional rights to exploit these natural resources lost.

Pollution that cannot be dispersed also affects riverine communities, as do sudden floods caused by dam breaches or emergency floodwater releases. Large reservoirs can also be breeding grounds for disease-carrying mosquitoes and water-dwelling parasites.

THE DAMNED
Impact of dams on river-basin inhabitants
2015 selected examples

■ existing dams and date completed

□ unfinished dams

⅃ dams where protest has been strong

👥 number of people displaced

Sobradinho, Bahia, Brazil, 1978

👥 **70,000**
Generated largest artificial lake in the world: 4,214 km². In 2008, 700 protesters occupied the hydroelectric plant to resolve outstanding land and environmental issues, and protest new river diversions.

Tucurui, Brazil 1975–85, 1998–2002

👥 **32,000 indigenous people**
100,000 affected by reduced water quality, loss of fisheries, and disease outbreaks. Protests continue.

Chixoy, Guatemala 1982

👥 **3,450 indigenous people**
6,000 households lost land, sacred sites, and access to local markets. Ten resistant communities massacred.

Itaipu, Paraná River, Paraguay and Brazil 1982

👥 **10,000 families**
One of 54 large dams in the La Plata basin; created a 200-km² reservoir and flooded 1,350 km² forests. Protests during construction led to formation of Dam-Affected Peoples Movement of Brazil (MAB), one of the world's strongest organizations protesting dams.

Belo Monte, Xingu, Brazil

👥 **20,000**
Work started in 2011 o the first of more than 4 dams planned for the Brazilian Amazon. The Belo Monte will divert 80% of the flow of the Xingu river, threatening the survival of indigenous peoples and other traditional communities.

Yacyretá, Argentina, Paraguay 1994

👥 **30,000 – 80,000**
Reservoir only half-filled because mitigation incomplete; major 2004 enquiry prompted by 4,000 affected families.

◀ 7 Environmental Security; 25 Dammed Rivers

Merowe, Sudan *2009*

♛ 50,000

Built with no environmental and health assessment; financed by Chinese and Arab investors. Displaced people were relocated away from the river, destroying their culture and livelihoods. Protests were met with extreme violence by Sudan's security forces.

Ilisu, Turkey

♛ 80,000

There has been huge international opposition to this project on the Tigris, which would result in the flooding of the medieval city of Hasankeyf, a massive displacement of people, and a heightening of tensions between the Turkish government and Kurdish residents. The site is now a militarized zone.

Kajbar, Sudan

♛ 10,000

The proposed dam will create a reservoir of 110 km². The displacement of 10,000 Nubians and destruction of 500 archaeological sites threatens the Nubian language and culture. Protests have been met by harsh measures by the Sudan security forces, including torture. A contract with Chinese company Sinohydro was signed in 2010.

Upper Yangtze, China

♛ 100,000 ethnic minority Naxi

After years of national and international protest, in March 2015 China's Ministry of Environmental Protection announced a ban on "the planning and construction of Xiaonanhai, Zhuyangxi and Shipeng dams or other barrage or dam projects within protected areas, including the mainstream of the Yangtze from Xiangjiaba dam to the Three Gorges dam, as well as its branches".

Three Gorges, Yangtze, China *2006*

♛ 1.13 million

This project submerged 13 cities, 140 towns and 1,350 villages. The compensation paid was inadequate and many resettled people live in poverty.

Son La, Vietnam *2012*

♛ 91,000

The resettlement of the ethnic minority people living along the Da river involved local people's committees, which addressed many issues. A pilot scheme was claimed to be a success, but ultimately it proved impossible to provide all resettled people with new land and livelihoods.

Nam Theun II, Laos *2008–09*

♛ 6,300

The resettlement programme was funded by the World Bank, and people now have better access to modern facilities, but they struggle to make a living on small, poor-quality land parcels. Fisher folk are faced with declining fish stocks and restricted access to the reservoir.

Bui Dam, Ghana

♛ 1,216

Under construction in Ghana. A community that refused to move was waiting for its case to be heard in 2015. Others have been given plots of land, but these, and the dwellings and other facilities, are entirely inadequate.

Sardar Sarovar, Gujarat, India

♛ 205,000+ by reservoir 157,000 by canals

This caused loss of biodiversity, forest and fishing rights, destruction of river-based livelihoods; 56% of those evicted are indigenous ethnic minorities. Despite failure to provide compensation for 40,000 families and continuing judicial appeals, the dam height is again being raised, from 122 to 139 metres.

Tipaimukh, Manipur, India

♛ at least 1,310 families (unverified)

A hydropower dam on the Barak River in fragile NE India, repeatedly proposed for construction in forestland, has so far been repeatedly turned down by the Environment Ministry. It would involve destroying 243 km² of forest and the way of life of indigenous people. Opposition has been intense and will continue.

Yali Falls, Vietnam *1996*

♛ 8,500 (Vietnam), 55,000 Cambodians' livelihoods affected

Downstream fisheries have been decimated, and flash flooding resulted from massive water releases. Public outcry led to (ineffective) impact mitigation efforts in 2001.

Manantali, Senegal River, Senegal *1987–2001*

♛ 12,000

Up to 800,000 people lost access to productive floodplains. 120 km² forest and 3,500 km² of downstream fish habitat destroyed. Funds ran out in 1988 before power station could be built; project re-activated in 1997, in atmosphere of bitter controversy.

Lesotho Highlands, Lesotho *2003*

♛ 30,000 approx.

Lost landholdings and inadequate compensation meant lost livelihoods. 150,000 downstream inhabitants suffer reduced river flows. Project increased, instead of solved, poverty in Lesotho.

Bargi, Madhya Pradesh, India *1990*

♛ 114,000

Chaotic submergence process; many villages relocated two or three times; no land-for-land compensation; loss of fishing rights; protests continue.

Pak Mun, Thailand *1991–94*

♛ 1,700 families

Persistent underestimation of those seriously affected. Major protests over many years led to a further 4,500 families being compensated in 2000. Pressure continues in Thailand to decommission the dam and scrap other dam and river diversion projects.

27 WATER POLLUTANTS

Globally, 2 million tons of sewage, industrial and agricultural waste are discharged into the world's waterways every year, polluting rivers, streams and wetlands, and wreaking devastation on coastal ecosystems.

An important pollutant is untreated human excreta. In the developing world as a whole, around 90 per cent of all wastewater is discharged untreated into watercourses, creating a major public health hazard. The caseload of illness connected to contaminated water occupies up to half the world's hospital beds.

Organic pollutants, which include not only sewage but food-processing waste, detergents, and industrial solvents, eventually decompose in water, but in so doing absorb vital oxygen, thereby depriving fish, plants and other aquatic creatures and causing their depletion. Those that resist environmental degradation through natural chemical and biological processes are classified as persistent organic pollutants (POPs). Many of these originate from pesticides, and are washed into streams by rainfall. They accumulate in human and animal tissue,

enter the food chain in concentrated form, and have serious repercussions on the health of living organisms. POPs can be found thousands of miles from their source, carried by tidal and wind currents into pristine environments such as the Antarctic.

Inorganic pollutants, such as detritus from the construction of roads and buildings, and the heavy metals lead, cadmium and mercury, typical by-products of the mining industry, never decompose and are found in the world's rivers, lakes and underground aquifers.

Where pollutants are discharged directly into waterways, there is the possibility of controlling them at the source through enforced regulation. Much harder to deal with are contaminants such as residues from cosmetics, antibiotics and other pharmaceutical products that find their way into the environment via human and animal excreta. Around 40 percent of antibiotics manufactured are fed to livestock as growth enhancers. These and many other pharmaceutical products are not eliminated by conventional wastewater treatment.

ORGANIC AND NON-ORGANIC POLLUTANTS

Pollution type	Main sources	Adverse effects
Organic matter e.g. excreta, food waste, carbon-based substances	Industrial wastewater and domestic sewage.	Decomposition leads to oxygen depletion, stressing or suffocating aquatic life.
Persistent organic compounds and micro-pollutants e.g. pesticides, cosmetics, pharmaceuticals, solvents	Industry, motor vehicles, agriculture, urban wastewater, urban run-off, municipal waste.	Changes in oxygen levels and decomposition rate of organic matter in water. Hormonal changes in organisms, including humans.
Heavy metals e.g. cadmium, lead, zinc, copper	Industries and mining sites.	Persist in sediments and wetlands. They poison fish and pass down food chain to humans.
Pathogens and microbes e.g. cryptospiridium, salmonella, shigella	Domestic sewage, livestock.	Spread of infectious diseases and parasites.
Nutrients e.g. nitrogen and phosphorus	Run-off from agricultural lands and urban areas, industrial discharge.	Over-stimulates growth of algae, which, when they decompose, use oxygen in water, stressing or suffocating aquatic life.

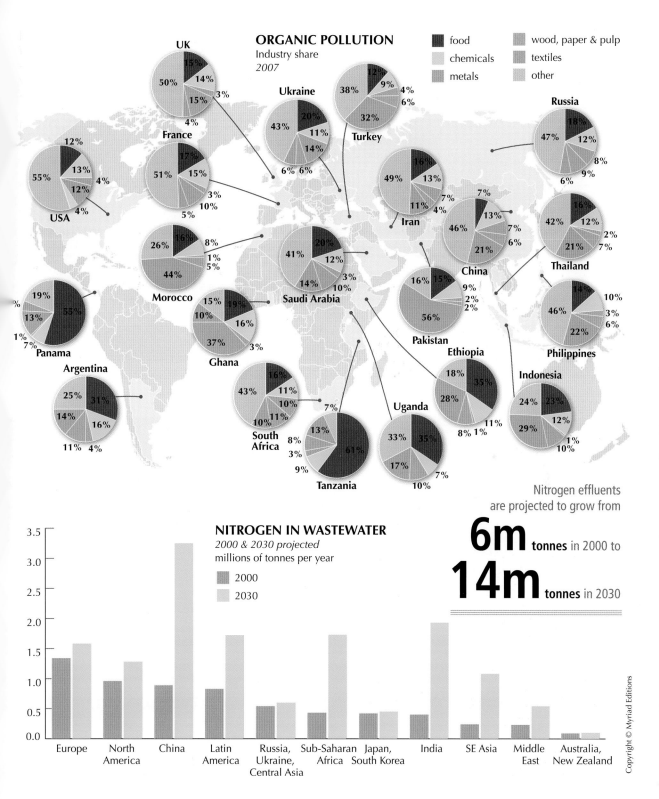

ORGANIC POLLUTION
Industry share
2007

Legend:
- food
- chemicals
- metals
- wood, paper & pulp
- textiles
- other

UK
15% 14% 3% 4% 15% 50%

Ukraine
20% 11% 14% 6% 6% 43%

Turkey
12% 9% 4% 6% 32% 38%

Russia
18% 12% 8% 9% 6% 47%

France
17% 15% 3% 10% 5% 51%

USA
12% 13% 4% 4% 55%

Iran
16% 13% 7% 4% 11% 49%

China
7% 13% 7% 6% 21% 46%

Thailand
16% 12% 2% 7% 21% 42%

Morocco
16% 8% 1% 5% 44% 26%

Saudi Arabia
20% 12% 3% 10% 14% 41%

Pakistan
15% 9% 2% 2% 56% 16%

Panama
19% 13% 1% 7% 55% %

Ghana
15% 19% 16% 3% 37% 10%

Philippines
14% 10% 3% 6% 22% 46%

Argentina
25% 31% 14% 16% 11% 4%

South Africa
16% 11% 10% 11% 10% 43%

Ethiopia
18% 35% 28% 8% 1% 11%

Indonesia
24% 23% 12% 1% 10% 29%

Uganda
33% 35% 17% 7% 10%

Tanzania
7% 13% 8% 3% 9% 61%

NITROGEN IN WASTEWATER
2000 & 2030 projected
millions of tonnes per year

- 2000
- 2030

Europe · North America · China · Latin America · Russia, Ukraine, Central Asia · Sub-Saharan Africa · Japan, South Korea · India · SE Asia · Middle East · Australia, New Zealand

Nitrogen effluents
are projected to grow from

6m tonnes in 2000 to
14m tonnes in 2030

28 WATER POLLUTION

There over

400

known

ocean dead zones
worldwide

High population density caused by rapid urbanization and accelerating industrialization, including mining enterprises and agri-businesses, is causing increased water pollution and corresponding environmental threats.

Human activity on an ever more crowded planet is over-burdening the world's in-built self-cleansing system. Of particular concern is the growth of urban populations and their high concentration in coastal areas, where many mega-cities are found. Inadequate urban infrastructure and management systems for dealing with polluted water exacerbate the problem.

Agricultural pollution, whereby run-off from fields flows into rivers and lakes with additional nutrients and contaminants from excess fertilizers and pesticides, is joined downstream by human and industrial contaminants. Heavily contaminated rivers create problems for the people who use the waters to wash in, cook with or even drink. And after entering lakes and seas their waters contribute to the creation of "dead zones", as the nutrients held in the fresh water feeds algae blooms, which in turn reduce the level of oxygen in the lake or sea to the point where no aquatic life can survive. These "dead zones" are growing; an estimated 245,000 square kilometres of marine ecosystems are affected, with inevitable impacts on fisheries, livelihoods and the food chain.

Groundwater contamination is even more problematic, but tends to be given less attention. Aquifers may be irreversibly damaged by toxic loads from solid waste tips or landfill; drains from industrial sites; farmyard drainage; leaking sewers or onsite sanitation systems; or by agricultural intensification, which leaves larger volumes of pesticides and fertilizer residues coating the ground.

Groundwater is widely depended on as a notionally clean source of drinking water. This promise is becoming more frequently compromised by leaching of pollutants or by the unexpected presence of naturally occurring toxic substances, such as arsenic in Bangladesh, or excessive fluoride in the Rift Valley and parts of South America, Asia and Japan. Cleaning groundwater up, or rendering it potable at the point of consumption, is complex, posing both technical and behavioural difficulties.

San Joaquin River

The waters of California's San Joaquin River are polluted by nitrates, phosphorus and selenium contained in agricultural run-off, and by chemicals from abandoned mines, while its natural "self-cleaning" mechanism – its once vast wetlands – have been largely destroyed by poor water flow and development. The San Joaquin basin provides drinking water for 4.5 million people, irrigation for more than 2m acres (800,000 hectares), and 3,000 megawatts of power, all of which result in a drastic reduction in flow and an increase in the concentration of pollutants.

Gulf of Mexico – coastal dead zone

The 3 million km² Mississippi basin includes some of the USA's most intensively farmed land. The nitrogen and phosphorus washed downriver from the fields and industries of the Midwest cause a bloom of algae at the river's mouth. As the algae decay, they use up oxygen, causing millions of bottom-dwelling sea creatures to die. In 2015, the area with very little dissolved oxygen was above average in size (red areas on image).

Baltic Sea – coastal dead zone

Spring and summer blooms of algae are a natural occurrence in the Baltic, but nutrient-enriched river water emptying into this relatively enclosed sea worsens the problem. The nine bordering countries have an agreement to cut pollution, overseen by the Helsinki Commission (HELCOM), but phosphorus and nitrogen continue to be discharged into the sea, albeit at lower rates in some areas in 2010–12 than in 1997–2003.

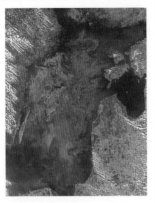

China – polluted rivers and aquifers

The poor state of China's water supply is notorious. Although 280m people did not have a safe drinking-water supply in 2015, there are, apparently, signs of gradual improvement, partly as a result of work by central and local government agencies, and partly due to pressure from citizen groups. In a 40-day campaign in North China in 2013, some 6.13 million yuan ($999,870) of fines were issued to 88 companies for violations resulting in underground water pollution, according to the Ministry of Environmental Protection.

CHINA'S WATER SUPPLY

Assessment by relevant Chinese government ministries.
2011

- ■ too polluted to be used
- ■ suitable only for industrial and agricultural use
- ■ source of drinking water; supports wildlife

key lakes and reservoirs

| 8% | 50% | 42% |

rivers

| 14% | 25% | 61% |

groundwater

| 15% | 40% | 45% |

India – human waste

Only 20% of India's sewage is treated before being discharged into waterways or deposited on land and seeping into groundwater. An estimated 40m litres are generated each day. No city in India has full sewerage; Delhi and Mumbai account for 40% of sewers in the country. Most people depend on septic-tank or pit toilets. Almost all groundwater, on which half of city dwellers depend for their household supply, has dangerous concentrations of nitrates. The Ganges is so heavily polluted by human and industrial waste that rates of gall bladder cancer along its banks are the second highest in the world.

Bangladesh – arsenic in wells

From the 1960s to the 1980s, the use of groundwater for drinking and domestic use was heavily promoted in Bangladesh as preferable to contaminated ponds, but the lowering of the water table, mainly due to heavy pumping for agricultural use, exposed naturally occurring arsenic seams that caused the water to become toxic.

This was first noticed in the early 1990s, when around 5m shallow tubewells were found to be unsafe, with at least 35m people exposed to poisoning. Since it can take time for the outcome to show itself in cancers and other conditions, the health crisis from arsenic contamination in Bangladesh will be long term.

Tigris and Euphrates under pressure

The loss of water in the Tigris–Euphrates basin due to increasing demand contributes to heightened pollution as the remaining flow is less able to absorb discharges. The flow of the Euphrates has been reduced by 40% after the construction of 32 dams and barrages. Along with growth in water-intensive agriculture, pesticide-use and industry, this has wreaked havoc on downstream water quality and ecology.

29 DAMAGED WATERWAYS

Industrialized society is damaging waterways. Modern lifestyles depend on mining, oil-drilling, energy-generation, chemicals, manufacturing processes and the storage and transportation of hazardous wastes.

People have always used air, land and water resources as "sinks" for disposal of waste. With industrialization, the volume and range of polluting agents has mounted, affecting the composition of surface water, groundwater and rainfall itself. As countries industrialize, their water-quality problems become ever more complex. They start with pathogens in sewage, then the introduction of pesticides through agro-chemical run-off, followed by the heavy metals, organic compounds, micro-pollutants and sediments included in industrial effluents.

Industries and mining sites are the worst polluters. "Tailings ponds" are used to store mining waste and as depositories for toxic by-products of industrial processes; these may leach their contents into the surrounding environment, or there can be accidental spillages. Acids from mining processes and power generation may also enter lakes and streams, and where they are released into the air they can acidify rain. Oil and other hazardous waste spillages occasionally occur on inland waterways.

A new disaster category, the "natech" disaster, has recently been identified, denoting a technological disaster triggered by a natural hazard. These are likely to occur when vulnerable installations are situated close to rivers which flood, or in earthquake-prone areas. Toxic materials may be released by a strong tremor, and safety precautions dependent on spraying be rendered ineffective when water and power sources fail.

Contaminated drinking water, Flint, USA

When Flint, Michigan switched the source of its water from Lake Huron to its local river in April 2014, the high levels of chloride (salt) in the river water caused out-dated pipes to corrode, and lead levels in the water to soar to an average 2,000 parts per billion (10 times the WHO recommended maximum). Many of the town's 100,000 residents drank contaminated water for many months before blood tests on children in August 2015 revealed dangerous levels of lead, putting them at high risk of brain damage. Residents had to rely on bottled water until the town's water source was reverted by order of the state governor.

Samarco mine, Brazil

The collapse of a dam holding back effluent from an iron-ore mine in Espirito Santo state, not only destroyed the village of Bento Rodrigues (shown here), killing 13 people, but released 60m m³ of waste containing high levels of toxic heavy metals and chemicals into the Rio Doce. The contaminated mud took 16 days to reach the sea, killing aquatic life and contaminating the drinking water of 250,000 people in the process.

Baia Mare tailings dam, Romania

In 2000, a dam holding back mine wastewater broke, releasing up to 100,000 m³ of cyanide-contamined water, as well as heavy metals into the Somes, Tisza and finally the Danube rivers and Black Sea. This interrupted the drinking-water supplies of 2.5 million people, and caused enormous damage to the river ecosystems, including the death of thousands of fish.

Aniline leak, China

Over New Year 2012–13 a leak from a faulty water hose in a fertilizer factory allowed 9 tonnes of potentially carcinogenic aniline to enter the river system and affect the drinking-water supply of a million people in Handan, Hebei province. The authorities were criticized for the delay in informing citizens of the problem.

Environmental activism, China

The Chinese are becoming increasingly adept at using social media to alert people to pollution incidents. In 2015, the Green Hunan group (shown here) drew attention to plans to create a reservoir to supply the citizens of Changsha with drinking water fed by a river into which raw sewage was discharged. The resulting public outcry and continued pressure from Green Hunan ensured that sewage-treatment facilities were completed before the reservoir was filled.

Earthquake, Turkey

In 1999, a powerful earthquake in northwest Turkey resulted in the release of hazardous materials, including the leakage of 6.5 million kg of toxic acrylonitrile (ACN), which contaminated air, soil and water, affecting residential areas.

Yamuna River, India

The Yamuna, once renowned for its "clear blue" water, and over which the Taj Mahal stands sentinel above Delhi at Agra, is now one of the most polluted in the world as it flows through India's capital.

Delhi produces **1,900 million litres** of sewage a day,

but only **54%** of this is being treated.

Out of **32** sewage treatment plants, **15** are working below their capacity.

This is because adequate drains needed to bring sewage to the treatment plants have **not been built**.

In the last two decades, **over $980 million** has been spent on cleaning the Yamuna River – **to little avail**.

In 2014, the Central Pollution Control Board stated that the polluted stretch of the Yamuna had increased from **500** to **600 km**, starting in Haryana, passing through Delhi, and on into Uttar Pradesh.

30 THREATENED ECOLOGIES

Even subtle changes in quality, temperature or seasonal availability of fresh water can have a devastating effect on the living organisms that inhabit it.

Freshwater environments are considered the most species-rich on earth, with complex ecologies that rely both on direct rainfall, and on water flows within and through them. They include rivers and lakes at a range of altitudes and latitudes, and many kinds of wetland.

A high proportion of plants, fish or other creatures in rivers, underground water systems, or lakes have evolved particular characteristics to suit the local ecology. Any change in that ecology threatens the extinction of these localized species.

Invasive plants and animals constitute a threat to native species, by competing for food and space, or even by killing and eating them. Canals providing navigational links between rivers spread species from one river basin to another, as do discharges of ballast water and the organisms it contains. Ecologies are also transformed by the submergence of previously farmed or forested land behind dams. River fragmentation by barrages and dams also slows flows and causes water temperatures to rise.

Non-native fish are often introduced by aquaculture, or released for recreational purposes. In over three-quarters of cases, this has led to a decline in native species. Invasive plants often crowd existing species out and reduce light and oxygen, altering the water chemistry and negatively affecting fish and other creatures. Water hyacinth, originally introduced worldwide as an ornamental species, is now found throughout the tropics, and is causing major environmental and economic problems.

Algae blooms on slow-flowing rivers or waterways filled with nutrient or pathogenic waste cause loss of species. Some algae are toxic, but even the non-toxic varieties deprive other water-dwelling organisms of oxygen when they decompose.

Biodiversity losses have been only partly detected and measured. Initially, monitoring tended to concentrate on larger organisms, such as mammals, birds, amphibians, reptiles and fish, but IUCN member organizations are seeking to broaden their assessments to smaller organisms, and invertebrates and plants in particular. In 2015 IUCN had data on 77,000 species, with a target of 160,000 species.

RELATIVE SPECIES RICHNESS
Ratio between species diversity and habitat extent

marine
0.2

terrestrial
2.7

freshwater
3.0

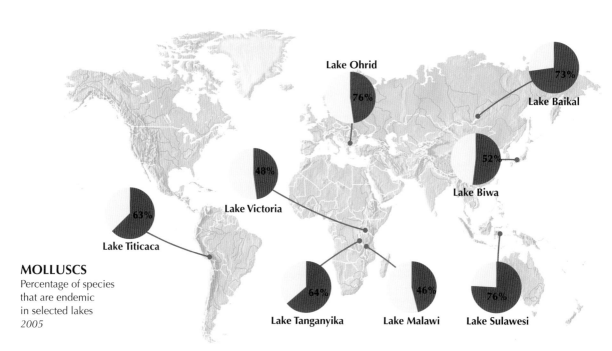

Lake Ohrid 76%

Lake Baikal 73%

Lake Biwa 52%

Lake Victoria 48%

Lake Titicaca 63%

Lake Tanganyika 64%

Lake Malawi 46%

Lake Sulawesi 76%

MOLLUSCS
Percentage of species that are endemic in selected lakes
2005

◄ *7 Environmental Security; 27 Water Pollutants; 28 Water Pollution; 29 Damaged Waterways*

	Species group	Status and trend	Percentage assessed by IUCN as threatened
	Waterbirds	More than 800 species of birds, including ducks, geese, herons and shorebirds, depend on wetlands for part of their lifecycle. They appear to be more threatened than any other group of birds. Migratory birds often travel thousands of kilometres, using wetlands as vital stopping off points during which they can feed and recuperate. The disappearance or degradation of just one area can seriously affect the birds that use them. Despite international legislation requiring countries to maintain favourable conditions for waders, populations of more than half of these bird species in western Europe are declining.	17%
	Wetland-dependent mammals	A range of mammals, including species of dolphin, otter, seal, shrew and hippopotamus, live or feed in fresh water. Of those assessed, over a third are threatened.	38%
	Freshwater amphibians	Species of amphibians that are associated with flowing water have a higher likelihood of being threatened than those that use still water.	26%
	Freshwater turtles	Of the 229 species assessed, 134 are threatened, with 32 of those considered critically endangered. Around three-quarters of Asia's species are threatened, the high value placed on them for their supposed medicinal qualities contributing to their demise.	59%
	Crocodiles	Of the 23 species that inhabit marshes, swamps, rivers, lagoons and estuaries, 7 are assessed as critically endangered.	48%
	Freshwater fish	Estimates of the number of freshwater fish species vary from 10,000 to 14,000 but what is certain is that a high proportion of them are threatened with extinction. The deliberate introduction of non-native species is very often the cause.	33%
	Freshwater crayfish and crabs	Many freshwater crayfish and crabs are threatened, not only by pollution and loss of habitat, but by invasive species that actively predate them, or out-compete them for food.	31%

PART 6   WATER FOR THE FUTURE

In the face of mounting pressures on the world's freshwater resources, the critical question for the future is how to handle a demand for water that is expected to rise by as much as 40 or 50 per cent within the next 20 years. According to a panel of leading experts, closing the approaching "water gap" will require a step-change improvement in water resource management, without which water poverty and insecurity will rise, environmental degradation worsen, and economic productivity falter.

Faced with a crisis on a global scale, optimists invariably bank on humanity's ingenuity and technological acumen to provide a solution. In the case of water, a miracle solution that remains out of reach is cheap desalination of seawater. But whatever technological breakthroughs may help augment supply or boost water use efficiency, the experts believe that the key to solving the global "water crisis" has more to do with creating a new political will around our most vital resource.

Working together to manage and distribute fairly whatever finite supply we possess is at the heart of all water-related policies today. As demands grow, users and providers are going to have to sit down together and negotiate fair shares. This will require more water diplomacy, more activity within river basin organizations, and more attempts to treat water in all its uses as a holistic common resource that has to be efficiently and equitably shared.

History has shown us that, faced with the need to co-operate over shared waters, humanity is up to the task. So far there has been no war over water. But institutional mechanisms for reconciling user and usage need be strengthened and respected at all levels, from the local to the international. In all adjudications over water, the rights of those who are least able to sustain their hold on the basis of their livelihood need special protection.

Even while ancient water-conservation systems are retooled, and new methods invented for recycling wastewater and maximizing "crop per drop", emphasis must be placed on sustaining our water commons. The deployment of market incentives has proved no panacea for better administration of water and sanitation services or resource conservation. Since water is essential to life itself, businesses surrounding it are not businesses like any other. Keeping this particular business clean, fair and efficient can only be done with powerful state commitment, sound regulatory regimes and real accountability.

Our Earth has been given a miraculously beneficent global water pot. Should we fail to conserve it we will have no-one to blame but ourselves.

31 TECHNOLOGICAL FIXES

Innovative check-dams

Check-dams are built by farmers throughout the Indian sub-continent to conserve rainwater after the monsoon and use it for irrigation. They are typically built with stones and mud; the idea of using plastic sheets over bare sand is an innovation. Community labour is often used, and everyone benefits from the raised water table.

New – and improved old – technologies for manipulating water can help address the increasing pressures on finite global water resources.

Around 10,000 years ago the well was a brilliant technological advance that made human settlement possible in places without rivers, lakes or springs. The need to deepen wells, build dams and channel water to manage its flow has prompted hydraulic innovation ever since. Treatment, desalination, and recycling are at the cutting edge of the new water *quality* technology portfolio.

Some technological approaches for water-short rain-fed agricultural zones are being rediscovered and updated after years of eclipse. Rainwater harvesting, using small check-dams in riverbeds, underground cisterns and roof-top collection tanks, has enjoyed a renaissance in many parts of the world. By contrast, massive engineering projects proposed for confining and channelling whole rivers across vast areas are less in the ascendant than they were.

Seawater desalination on a large scale is still prohibitively expensive for poorer countries, with reverse osmosis technology consuming a vast amount of energy: between 4 and 25 kWh (kilowatt hours) for every cubic metre of fresh water. Recent breakthroughs in membrane chemistry have, however, pushed down the cost of desalinated water from $1 per cubic metre to between $0.80 and $0.50.

A solution being explored in Singapore that would propel desalination into a new era is biomimicry: trying to understand and copy the osmotic mechanisms that enable mangrove plants and certain fish to survive in fresh, briny or salt water.

Technological advances can also help prevent disease. Low-cost water purification using nanotechnology to filter out microbes, bacteria and contaminants that endanger health could revolutionize the safety of mains water supplies in countries such as India.

USA
Every state now has at least one desalination plant.

DESALINATION

Capacity of desalination plants
latest available data 2000–15
cubic metres per day

1 cubic metre (m³) = 1,000 litres

■ 1 million – 3 million	fewer than 10,000
■ 100,000 – 547,000	no data
■ 10,000 – 99,000	

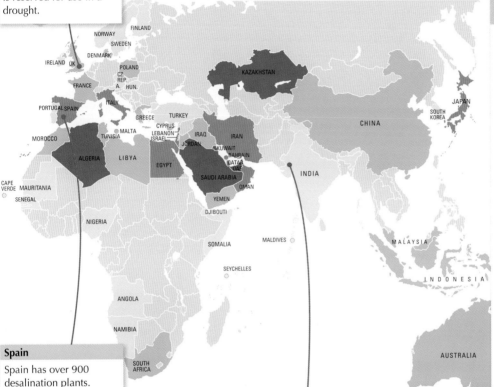

Tackling excessive fluoride

High levels of fluoride
can occur naturally in
groundwater, causing
illness and skeletal
deformity. In India
alone, around 60
million people are
affected. Technologies
have been developed
to filter out excess
fluoride at village
level or in smaller
household filters
(shown here), in
which water is passed
through removable
columns of alumina
granules. Water
monitoring and filter
recharging can be
managed by the
community with
training and support.
Loss of aches and
pains and improved
well-being provide
powerful incentives.

Spain

Spain has over 900
desalination plants.

Intelligent irrigation

More efficient use of water in food
production requires a new mind-set in the
water industry. "Intelligent irrigation" uses
precision systems, with high-tech
instruments for measuring, monitoring and
forecasting. Water can be delivered directly
to the plant base, and used more sparingly
to produce smaller, but just as flavourful,
fruit and veg. Plant varieties are being
developed that require less water.

Growing food in carefully calibrated
environments is another innovation. For
example, seawater can be used to cool and
humidify special greenhouses (shown here),
thus reducing the amount of fresh water
needed for actual irrigation.

91

Despite its status as a vital resource to which all must have access, water has been commodified in recent decades and transformed from a non-market to a market good that has to be paid for.

The catalyst for this change was the mounting realization that the world's freshwater resources were not being managed efficiently and that increased value must be attached to water conservation. In 1992, the idea of water as an "economic good" gained international acceptance. Thereafter, the sale of water at a price capable of covering the costs of service delivery, and the privatization of water utilities in developing countries, were actively promoted under World Bank–IMF auspices. The assumption was that the application of market principles would miraculously conserve water, improve efficiency and increase service spread.

The increasing costs of water services, especially to expanding cities whose nearby aquifers and surface sources are being rapidly exhausted, is undeniable. But proponents of water as a human right protest that its commodification allows corporate interests to make a profit from what should be a common asset, while depriving low-income groups access to a vital resource. The debate is not to do with whether the costs of water services are rising, but whether governments should be obliged to subsidize supplies to ensure universal access.

The growing involvement of water companies in service provision has not proved the panacea its proponents expected. In most developing countries, price hikes sufficient to achieve full cost recovery – whether from farmers drawing water for irrigation or domestic consumers – are not politically feasible. Sound water-management systems cannot be achieved solely by market reforms, especially in environments with many vested, corruption-prone and unaccountable interests. The complexities are too great and the margins for profitability too small.

Privatization or no privatization, the challenge of spreading affordable services to low-income consumers persists, as does the need to address water conservation by all available means, including market incentives.

AS SUPPLIES DIMINISH, COSTS INCREASE

As water tables drop and sources close to urban centres dry up, increasing power is needed to pump water from deeper levels or more distant sources. Mexico City is forced to pump water a distance of 150 kilometres and up 1,100 metres from the Cutzamala River, using electricity estimated to cost $65m a year.

Jakarta has so depleted its underground aquifers that seawater has seeped 15 kilometres inland, making the supply saline and causing some metal structures to collapse due to corrosion.

The more powerful pumps needed to raise deeper water increase the cost, or make the task impossible. Small-scale farmers in developing countries may find their cheap pumps no longer up to the job. US farmers and water companies are more likely to make the necessary investment, but may still find that the additional cost renders crops uneconomic.

Power plants dependent on water to cool them may need to make expensive adjustments to their water intakes to cope with dropping water levels. Diminished water flow will reduce the amount of electricity generated by hydropower plants, making it more expensive.

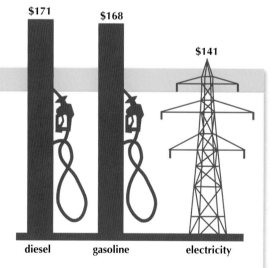

diesel   gasoline   electricity

$171 $168 $141

COST OF WATER EXTRACTION FOR IRRIGATION
Average of 17 Western States, USA
2008
$ per hectacre

Right2Water: Ireland erupts

In August 2015, 80,000 protesters marched through Dublin in protest at water charges introduced as part of Ireland's austerity deal with Europe. The bailout plan of 2010, backed by the European Central Bank, IMF and EU, required that Irish Water impose high domestic water charges to boost state revenues. The issue of water charges prompted more opposition to austerity measures in Ireland than any other.

Critics objected that the charges were having a catastrophic effect on poorer members of society whilst barely impinging on the lives of the better-off. This was the fifth such protest organized by umbrella group Right2Water within 12 months. Protests demanding that the country's water supply remain in public hands continued into 2016.

Tanzania

Privatization of water services was imposed on the Tanzanian government as a condition of IMF and World Bank debt relief and concessionary loans, and UK aid was used to support the privatization process. A subsidiary of the UK company Biwater took on the contract in Dar es Salaam in 2003. The Tanzanian government cancelled the contract after less than two years, citing failure to meet the contract targets. A Biwater company then took the government to the International Centre for the Settlement of Investment Disputes court and sought $20 million damages for breach of contract.
The case failed.

WATER PRIVATIZATION
Selected examples

Manila, Philippines

An example of the supposed efficiency gains from privatizing water utilities was Manila, for which the World Bank's International Finance Corporation (IFC) designed a 25-year, $2.7 billion concession in 1997. The outcome is hotly debated. The IFC claim that 1.7 million extra people have gained access to a supply at a price lower than that charged by private vendors. Critics claim that the service is poor, and price-hikes are far too frequent. "We are in a vicious cycle", a Manila Water director lamented. "Government can't increase the rates because customers are dissatisfied; and they won't pay so income is low and the service cannot be improved."

Bolivia

The most famous case of protest against water privatization took place in Cochabamba, Bolivia, in 1999–2000. A local company, Aguas del Tunari, owned by the US company Bechtel, was given a monopoly to collect water charges. The company took over water systems constructed and run by householders and small independent co-operatives without compensation. Prices shot up and citizens were forced to pay for collecting their own rain. Months of simmering protest led to the occupation of the city square by 80,000 people. The government sent in troops. Street battles ensued and Aguas del Tunari fled the country.

Guyana

In early 2007, the Guyanese authorities cancelled a five-year water management contract with Severn Trent Water International (STWI). The UK aid budget had been used to pay company fees for the contract and for privatization consultants, thanks to a policy commitment to utility privatization and favour for home-based companies. The Guyanese audited STWI's performance, and found that only a tiny proportion of those supposed to receive potable water by 2005 had done so. Altogether, the company failed to meet five out of seven objectives in the contract. Subsequently, STWI pulled out of a bid for a similar contract in Nepal.

WATER SUPPLY FOR AMERINDIAN SETTLEMENTS

80% supposed to receive it by 2005

4% had done so by 2006

A human right

People cannot live without water. Thus, the right to water is regarded as integral to the right to life. However, it is one thing to declare a human right in international law, and another to see it acted upon. The UN Human Rights Council has a Special Rapporteur whose job is to monitor and assist states' realization of their citizens' water and sanitation rights.

The right to a supply of drinking water (and to sanitation) is gradually being incorporated into national laws and constitutional amendments. South Africa, for example, has set a legal obligation for households to receive a certain amount of safe water free of charge.

More than 260 river basins are shared between countries, and equitable use of their waters requires negotiation and agreement.

Diplomacy over shared waters has a long history. Unlike land, which can be demarcated, water does not stay still. Governments and legal systems have therefore accepted that the content of rivers and aquifers is a communal asset over which ownership cannot be asserted. But since political boundaries are rarely defined by river basin – in fact rivers often act as boundaries – the sharing of waters between up- and downstream nations presents particular challenges.

Upstream fragmentation by dams, extraction of large volumes of water, and alteration in flow and water quality are among the issues requiring diplomacy, with disputes usually settled within specially established frameworks. Some international river basin organizations – for example, that for the Nile – remain in more or less permanent session, addressing issues as they are brought to the table by the countries involved.

The development of international water law has advanced in recent years. Since water became recognized as an economic good, provoking fears that it might be priced beyond the reach of poorer communities, a forceful attempt was made to establish a right to water. In 2010, the UN General Assembly formally recognized the right to water and sanitation. This was followed by a UN Human Rights Council resolution affirming that these rights are part of existing international law, and calling on states to take action to provide universal access to safe water and sanitation.

In 1997, the UN passed a Convention on the Law of the Non-Navigational Uses of International Watercourses. This establishes overarching principles to be followed in the negotiation of watercourse treaties and the legal settlement of transboundary water disputes. This Convention entered into international law in 2014 following its 35th ratification, and now has 36 states parties.

13
river basins
are shared by
5 or more
countries

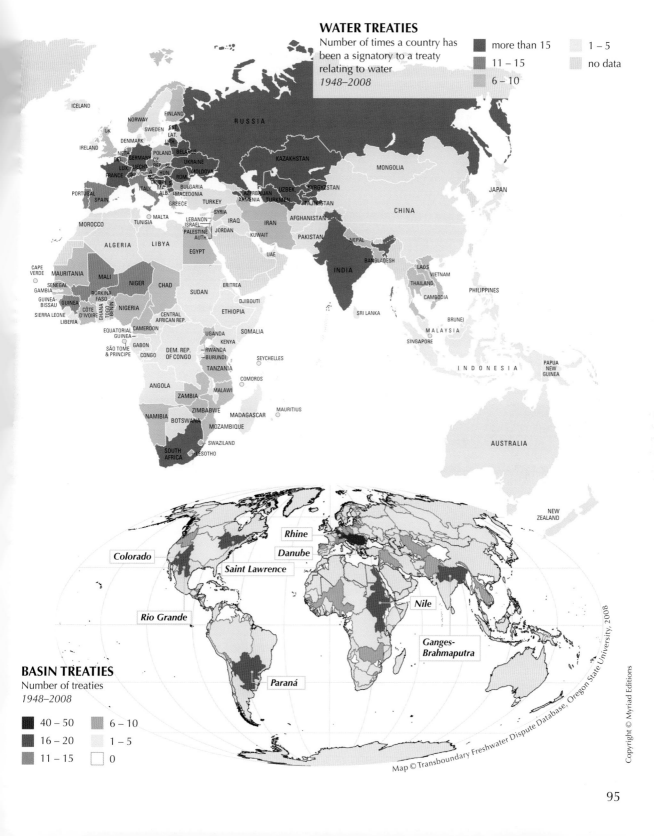

WATER TREATIES

Number of times a country has been a signatory to a treaty relating to water
1948–2008

- more than 15
- 11 – 15
- 6 – 10
- 1 – 5
- no data

ICELAND
NORWAY
FINLAND
SWEDEN
EST.
LAT.
LITH.
UK
DENMARK
IRELAND
NETH.
BEL.
LUX.
LIECHT.
FRANCE
GERMANY
POLAND
CZ.
REP.
ST.
HUN.
BELARUS
UKRAINE
MOLDOVA
RUSSIA
KAZAKHSTAN
MONGOLIA
JAPAN
PORTUGAL
SPAIN
ITALY
MALTA
ALB.
SL.
CR.
SERB.
ROM.
BULGARIA
MACEDONIA
GREECE
TURKEY
AZERBAIJAN
ARMENIA
TURKMEN.
UZBEK.
KYRGYZSTAN
TAJIKISTAN
CHINA
MOROCCO
TUNISIA
LEBANON
ISRAEL
PALESTINE
AUTH.
JORDAN
SYRIA
IRAQ
IRAN
AFGHANISTAN
KUWAIT
UAE
PAKISTAN
NEPAL
BANGLADESH
INDIA
LAOS
VIETNAM
THAILAND
CAMBODIA
PHILIPPINES
BRUNEI
MALAYSIA
SINGAPORE
SRI LANKA
ALGERIA
LIBYA
EGYPT
CAPE VERDE
MAURITANIA
MALI
NIGER
CHAD
SUDAN
ERITREA
DJIBOUTI
ETHIOPIA
SENEGAL
GAMBIA
GUINEA-BISSAU
GUINEA
SIERRA LEONE
LIBERIA
CÔTE D'IVOIRE
BURKINA FASO
GHANA
TOGO
BENIN
NIGERIA
CENTRAL AFRICAN REP.
EQUATORIAL GUINEA
CAMEROON
SÃO TOME & PRINCIPE
GABON
CONGO
DEM. REP. OF CONGO
UGANDA
RWANDA
BURUNDI
KENYA
SOMALIA
TANZANIA
SEYCHELLES
COMOROS
ANGOLA
ZAMBIA
MALAWI
MOZAMBIQUE
NAMIBIA
ZIMBABWE
BOTSWANA
MADAGASCAR
MAURITIUS
SWAZILAND
SOUTH AFRICA
LESOTHO
INDONESIA
PAPUA NEW GUINEA
AUSTRALIA
NEW ZEALAND

Rhine
Danube
Colorado
Saint Lawrence
Rio Grande
Nile
Ganges-Brahmaputra
Paraná

BASIN TREATIES

Number of treaties
1948–2008

- 40 – 50
- 16 – 20
- 11 – 15
- 6 – 10
- 1 – 5
- 0

Map © Transboundary Freshwater Dispute Database, Oregon State University, 2008

WATER ISSUES

Co-operation and
conflict
by type of issue
1948–2008

- ■ quantity
- ■ joint management
- ■ infrastructure
- ■ quality
- ■ hydropower
- ■ flood control
- ■ technical co-operation
- ■ other

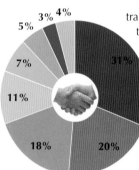

Total co-operative events: 1,705

3% 4%
5%
7%
11%
18%
20%
31%

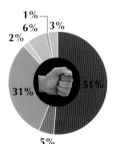

Total conflictual events: 759

1%
6% 3%
2%
31% 51%
5%

The spectre of growing competition between states over water has generated fighting talk, especially in retaliation against upstream behaviour. But there is a more optimistic scenario.

Nearly 450 international agreements were signed between 1820 and 2007 over shared water, which have been respected even when relations between states have been seriously strained. For example, the 1960 Indus Waters Treaty, dividing the waters of the joint basin between India and Pakistan, has held out, despite two subsequent wars. So far, no threat has ever been made by upstream India to suspend water releases.

Managing shared waters successfully within transnational river basin organizations has tended to benefit all parties by protecting water quality, controlling floods, instituting joint monitoring and early warning systems, and agreeing wastewater emissions. But as pressures grow, deeper and more systematic co-operation is needed.

Africa has the most politically dispersed rivers and lakes: 90 per cent of all surface water in the continent is in transboundary basins, and these are inhabited by 75 per cent of its people. The Nile basin is the hardest to adjudicate, with two out of 10 basin members – Egypt and Sudan – heavily dependent on the waters of a river whose final 2,700 kilometre journey is through entirely rainless desert.

River basins in the Middle East, including the Jordan, the Tigris and the Euphrates, urgently need enhanced co-operation, since upstream extractions are causing deep antagonism. Turkey, unlike Jordan and Iraq, is not a party to the UN Convention on Non-navigable uses of International Watercourses and is engaged on an upstream Tigris–Euphrates dam-building spree.

Colorado
USA
MEXICO

The Colorado

A 1944 USA–Mexico Treaty guaranteed Mexico 1.8bn m³ a year of water from the Colorado, but did not define the water *quality*. In the 1950s, as the USA increasingly diverted the river to newly developed areas, the river water released to Mexico became more saline. In 1973 an international agreement interpreted the 1944 treaty as guaranteeing Mexico the same water quality as that used in the USA, and a desalination plant was built. In 2012 it was agreed that the USA would send Mexico less water during drought years, and store water for Mexico behind US dams during wet years. In March and April 2014, under the "Minute 319" agreement, water was released from the Moreles Dam, mimicking the natural spring flood, sending water down the final 113 km to the delta for the first time since 1998 (see photo).

CONFLICT AND CO-OPERATION

Number and type of events related to
transboundary river basins
1948–2008
Total: 2,586 events

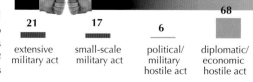

21	17	6	68
extensive military act	small-scale military act	political/ military hostile act	diplomatic/ economic hostile act

◄ *6 Competition and Conflict*

The Danube

The Soviet Union dominated the basin from 1945 until its collapse in the early 1990s, at which point the Danube became the most internationalized basin in the world. It was also severely polluted. In 1994, the Danube Convention was signed and an international commission established. This now has 14 country members, plus the EU. Over $3 billion has been used to bring about a significant ecological recovery in the basin, and a doubling of aquatic species from 1980 levels.

Tigris–Euphrates basin

Iraq and Syria depend on the waters of this basin for two-thirds of their water. Plans by Turkey to build 22 new dams and irrigation works will drastically reduce the flow to both countries.

The Indus

There have been calls for "water jihad" from some people in Pakistan complaining about dams being built by India on the upper reaches of the Indus river system. India's response is that it is not exceeding the take-off levels permitted under the 1960 Indus Water Treaty, and that Pakistan is wasting 35% of its share by inefficient management. Renewed co-operation on water could ease relations generally.

The Mekong

The Mekong rises on the Tibetan plateau, and flows through six countries. More than 60m people in the Lower Mekong basin depend on its waters for food, livelihood and transport. A Mekong River Commission was formed in 1995 between Cambodia, Laos, Thailand and Vietnam. Although China is an official Dialogue Partner, it is constructing dams on the upper reaches without consulting the Commission, and threatening serious impacts downstream.

Lake Chad

Failure of the states bordering the lake to engage in joint management has contributed to an environmental disaster, leaving it one-tenth the size it was 40 years ago.

The Nile

The Nile Waters Agreement (1929, re-affirmed 1954) set down the rights of Egypt and Sudan to the river water, but decolonization in the 1960s led to the basin being shared by 10 countries. In 2010, the Nile Basin Initiative presented a Cooperative Framework Agreement, introducing the concept of equitable water allocation, but Egypt and Sudan refused to sign, unwilling to lose their special status. However, the Khartoum Declaration of March 2015, in which Egypt recognized Ethiopia's right to dam the Blue Nile, is a positive step towards further co-operation.

Map labels: Danube, Drava, Sava, SLO., A., SL., H., CRO, B-H, M., SERB., UKRAINE, Tisza, ROMANIA, Danube, TURKEY, SYRIA, Tigris, Euphrates, ISRAEL, PALESTINE AUTHORITY, JORDAN, IRAQ, Jordan, EGYPT, Nile, NIGER, CHAD, Lake Chad, SUDAN, ERITREA, NIGERIA, CENTRAL AFRICAN REP., CAM., DEM. REP. OF CONGO, UGANDA, KENYA, RWANDA, BURUNDI, TANZANIA, ETHIOPIA, PAKISTAN, Indus, Ganges, Brahmaputra, NEPAL, Meghna, INDIA, BANGLADESH, MYANMAR, LAOS, THAILAND, CAMBODIA, VIETNAM, Lower Mekong, Mekong, Upper, CHINA

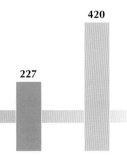

Chart values:

strong/official verbal hostility	227
mild/unofficial verbal hostility	420
neutral, non-significant act	122
mild verbal support	682
official verbal support	276
cultural, scientific agreement/support	242
economic, technical, industrial agreement	334
military, economic strategic support	7
international water treaty	164

35 MANAGING THE FUTURE

40%

of respondents

to World Economic
Forum survey in 2015
considered future

**global
water crises**

of major concern

The real world water crisis is a crisis of water management. We cannot manufacture water, nor expect to discover bottomless wells deep inside the Earth. So, for the future, we must manage what we have better, dividing it fairly and efficiently between different types of usage.

Integrated water resources management (IWRM) has a geographical dimension, emphasizing the river basin as the logical unit of strategic planning. It also encompasses environmental protection, food security, appropriate choices regarding water use in economic productivity, good governance, equitable pricing policies and reform of water-managing institutions.

Water resources management in different spheres – agriculture, industry, public health – can no longer be fragmented and left to competing private and public institutions. But while this principle has been widely recognized, there is a long way to go before integrated systems of management are fully realized.

Finding a route to that ideal in which the needs of different users are moderated according to an agreed framework of priorities, is the only way to attain water security at household, community, national and international level. A concerted effort will be needed by all stakeholders, along with a willingness to adopt a holistic view of the total resource and the many demands upon it.

The emphasis on sound management now resonates in all international water policy proposals, including in Sustainable Development Goal No 6, to "Ensure availability and sustainable management of water and sanitation for all".

The internationally driven effort to bring all sectors concerned with water together and promote dialogue between users and providers is extremely complex, since it cuts across many vested interests and political or commercial agendas.

However, if the growing "water gaps" are to be bridged, a policy of conservation, efficient utility, and respect for humanity's needs in a co-operative spirit will be essential. Water's vital role in supporting life should be a means of building that spirit, within and between societies.

Armenia: local solutions for wastewater management

After the collapse of the Soviet Union, an energy crisis led to the closure of wastewater pumping stations. In Parakar village, discharge of wastewater into an irrigation canal contaminated cultivated fields, jeopardizing food safety and health. Agriculture, water services and health were administratively separate, and no centrally planned solution seemed practicable. In 2010, with support from a partnership network, Parakar community introduced a lagoon-type wastewater-treatment system, the first of its kind in Armenia. This has led the way in community IWRM solutions, and ensured that Parakar's domestic wastewater is now treated to a level safe for irrigation use.

Cameroon: protecting Lake Ossa

Nine lakes and 20 islands make up the Lake Ossa complex, providing 80% of the local population with their livelihood. Due to over-fishing, destruction of habitat for clams and mussels, water-quality deterioration from chemical run-off, and fluctuating water flows caused by the National Electricity Corporation, these livelihoods were threatened. This prompted further over-exploitation of fish and mollusc beds. In response, the NGO Watershed Task Group brought all parties together for a series of meetings, and enrolled the stakeholders into a common plan. As a result, industrial contamination has been reduced, wetland conservation adopted, and 12 user associations started up and trained in supplementary occupations.

◀ *3 Water Shortage; 4 Rising Demand; 5 Dwindling Supply*

SURVEY OF INTEGRATED WATER RESOURCES MANAGEMENT
Countries classified according to
Human Development Index (HDI) group
2011

Respondents to 2012
UN survey in:

- very high HDI group
- high HDI group
- medium HDI group
- low HDI group
- non-respondent to survey

SURVEY RESPONSE: STATUS OF MAIN PLANS
for integrated approaches
to water resources management
by HDI group *2011*

- fully implemented
- being implemented
- in development/developed
- not relevant

very high	14%	38%	46%	2%
high	6%	36%	56%	3%
medium	3%	48%	45%	3%
low	9%	25%	66%	

Women and water management

Women's role in managing drinking water and sanitation services, including carrying out equipment maintenance and minor repairs, can be important.

Village women normally have to collect household water and deal with sanitation and waste disposal, so they have a greater vested interest in service performance than men, and frequently take a lead in local water and sanitation committees. The introduction of sound water management practices in low-income areas should therefore include women's participation.

PROGRESS ON IWRM PLANNING
Status of national/federal IWRM plans
2008 & 2012

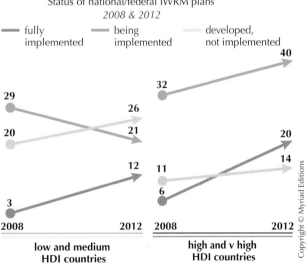

- fully implemented
- being implemented
- developed, not implemented

low and medium HDI countries

2008   2012

29
20
3

26
21
12

high and v high HDI countries

2008   2012

32
11
6

40
20
14

Copyright © Myriad Editions

99

PART 7   DATA TABLES AND SOURCES

In recent years, extraordinary efforts have been made by the international system to improve the quality of information available on all sorts of subjects, including water. Policies and programmes, decision-makers increasingly insist, must be "evidence-based"; yet one of the characteristics of a "developing" country, or an underdeveloped area within a better-off country, is that evidence is lacking. So at the same time as trying to make sound decisions about where and how to spend resources, on water as well as in all sorts of other human-development contexts, it is also necessary to improve the means of collecting and analysing the data on which such decisions have to be made.

Despite the progress of recent years, data gathering in the water context remains far from perfect. For one thing, the range of subject areas – from meteorology to health, from industrial pollution to irrigation – is so vast. Attempts to collect better information – as has been done by UNESCO's "World Water Assessment Programme" for presentation in the UN's World Water Reports – can still reveal that we know far less about a subject than we thought. Accurate statistics about the rate of loss of freshwater fish species, for example, or the number of people annually affected by water-related diseases, are elusive. The Joint Monitoring Programme of WHO and UNICEF, which has as its strategic objective to improve monitoring of progress towards the fulfilment of the water and sanitation Sustainable Development Goals, has discovered many anomalies in the ways countries collect data and report on their services.

The purposes of information-gathering and presentation differ, and information may carry a political charge. The discovery of arsenic in groundwater in Bangladesh caused a furore: who covered this information up or failed to address it in good time? Similarly, estimates of water quantities flowing in major rivers and the amount of take-off by upstream users have huge potential for dispute. Tallies of how many people are losing out on access to standpipes or toilets may miscount the number needing improvements. Populations squatting illegally on land designated "agricultural" may be left out altogether, even though they have been there for decades. In all cases, averages – of water consumption, water use in agriculture, pollutant discharge – on a per capita basis by country distort the real state of affairs for almost everyone.

Any presentation of data in the format of an atlas is additionally circumscribed by the requirement to express information in a way to which it may not easily lend itself. Water primarily occurs in river basins, not in countries. Water's physical presence defines the nature of human settlement, economic activity, and patterns of life. Yet all the data connected to the availability of the resources, and its use and misuse, reflects a different and often unconnected arrangement of human society in nation states. Water is truly one of the most pervasive and problematical substances on the planet, and one of the hardest to understand on a country-by-country basis, both statistically and analytically.

NEEDS AND RESOURCES

	1 Total population millions		2 Urban population as % of total		3 Improved water source % of population with access 2015	4 Improve sanitatio % of popula with acce 2014
	2015	2030 projected	2015	2030 projected		
Afghanistan	32.53	43.85	26%	34%	55%	32%
Albania	2.90	2.95	63%	77%	95%	93%
Algeria	39.67	48.27	72%	78%	84%	87%
Angola	25.02	39.35	40%	48%	49%	51%
Antigua and Barbuda	0.09	0.10	24%	21%	98%	–
Argentina	43.42	49.36	89%	89%	99%	96%
Armenia	3.02	2.99	62%	63%	100%	90%
Australia	23.97	28.48	89%	91%	100%	100%
Austria	8.54	8.84	66%	70%	100%	100%
Azerbaijan	9.75	10.73	54%	58%	87%	88%
Bahamas	0.39	0.45	83%	85%	98%	92%
Bahrain	1.38	1.64	88%	90%	100%	99%
Bangladesh	161.00	186.46	34%	45%	87%	60%
Barbados	0.28	0.29	32%	34%	100%	96%
Belarus	9.50	8.98	75%	77%	100%	94%
Belgium	11.30	12.02	97%	95%	100%	100%
Belize	0.36	0.47	43%	44%	100%	91%
Benin	10.88	15.59	44%	51%	78%	20%
Bhutan	0.77	0.89	39%	49%	100%	50%
Bolivia	10.72	13.18	70%	76%	90%	50%
Bosnia and Herzegovina	3.81	3.58	40%	46%	100%	95%
Botswana	2.26	2.82	52%	52%	96%	63%
Brazil	207.85	228.66	84%	86%	98%	83%
Brunei Darussalam	0.42	0.50	78%	81%	–	–
Bulgaria	7.15	6.30	74%	77%	99%	86%
Burkina Faso	18.11	27.24	30%	40%	82%	19%
Burundi	11.18	17.36	12%	16%	76%	48%
Cambodia	15.58	18.99	21%	26%	76%	41%
Cameroon	23.34	32.95	54%	62%	76%	46%
Canada	35.94	40.39	82%	85%	100%	100%
Cape Verde	0.52	0.61	64%	68%	92%	72%
Central African Republic	4.90	6.49	39%	45%	69%	22%
Chad	14.04	21.95	22%	25%	51%	12%
Chile	17.95	20.25	89%	89%	99%	99%
China	1,376.05	1,415.55	57%	71%	96%	75%
Colombia	48.23	53.18	78%	86%	91%	81%
Comoros	0.79	1.08	28%	31%	90%	36%
Congo	4.62	6.79	66%	71%	77%	28%
Congo, Dem Rep	77.27	120.30	39%	43%	52%	15%
Cook Islands	0.02	0.02	75%	77%	–	–
Costa Rica	4.81	5.41	80%	91%	98%	95%
Côte d'Ivoire	22.70	32.14	51%	57%	82%	22%
Croatia	4.24	3.98	59%	65%	100%	97%
Cuba	11.39	11.24	76%	77%	95%	93%
Cyprus	1.17	1.30	67%	68%	100%	100%
Czech Republic	10.54	10.46	75%	79%	100%	99%
Denmark	5.67	6.00	88%	90%	100%	100%
Djibouti	0.89	1.05	78%	81%	90%	47%

5 Total renewable water resources m³ per person per year 2014	6 Total renewable water resources million m³ 2014	7 Water dependency % of water originating outside country 2014	8 Annual renewable groundwater million m³ 2014	9 Annual renewable surface water million m³ 2014	
2,088	65,330	29%	55,680	10,650	Afghanistan
9,482	30,200	11%	26,350	6,200	Albania
292	11,670	4%	10,150	1,517	Algeria
6,704	148,400	0%	145,400	58,000	Angola
571	52	0%	–	0	Antigua and Barbuda
20,960	876,200	67%	860,200	128,000	Argentina
2,604	7,769	12%	4,858	4,311	Armenia
20,821	492,000	0%	440,000	72,000	Australia
9,113	77,700	29%	77,700	6,000	Austria
3,645	34,680	77%	32,520	6,510	Azerbaijan
1,828	700	0%	–	0	Bahamas
86	116	97%	4	112	Bahrain
7,741	1,227,000	91%	1,206,000	21,120	Bangladesh
280	80	0%	8	74	Barbados
6,220	57,900	41%	57,900	15,900	Belarus
1,642	18,300	34%	18,300	900	Belgium
63,912	21,730	30%	21,730	7,510	Belize
2,490	26,390	61%	26,090	1,800	Benin
101,828	78,000	0%	78,000	8,100	Bhutan
52,913	574,000	47%	547,900	130,000	Bolivia
9,804	37,500	5%	36,340	11,570	Bosnia and Herzegovina
6,003	12,240	80%	10,640	1,700	Botswana
42,800	8,647,000	35%	8,647,000	645,600	Brazil
20,095	8,500	0%	8,500	100	Brunei Darussalam
2,972	21,300	1%	20,400	6,400	Bulgaria
775	13,500	7%	9,000	9,500	Burkina Faso
1,196	12,540	20%	12,540	7,470	Burundi
30,900	476,100	75%	471,500	17,600	Cambodia
12,406	283,100	4%	278,100	100,000	Cameroon
81,689	2,902,000	2%	2,892,000	370,000	Canada
595	300	0%	181	124	Cape Verde
29,943	141,000	0%	141,000	56,000	Central African Republic
3,459	45,700	67%	44,200	11,500	Chad
51,938	923,100	4%	923,100	140,000	Chile
1,993	2,840,000	1%	2,739,000	828,800	China
48,232	2,360,000	9%	2,360,000	510,000	Colombia
1,596	1,200	0%	200	1,000	Comoros
182,496	832,000	73%	832,000	122,000	Congo
18,498	1,283,000	30%	1,282,000	421,000	Congo, Dem Rep
–	–	0%	–	0	Cook Islands
22,884	113,000	0%	113,000	37,310	Costa Rica
4,044	84,140	9%	81,300	37,840	Côte d'Ivoire
24,696	105,500	64%	95,000	11,000	Croatia
3,386	38,120	0%	31,640	6,480	Cuba
677	780	0%	560	410	Cyprus
1,224	13,150	0%	13,150	1,430	Czech Republic
1,064	6,000	0%	3,700	4,300	Denmark
339	300	0%	300	15	Djibouti

NEEDS AND RESOURCES

	1 Total population millions		2 Urban population as % of total		3 Improved water source % of population with access 2015	4 Improved sanitation % of population with access 2014
	2015	2030 projected	2015	2030 projected		
Dominica	0.07	0.08	70%	74%	–	–
Dominican Republic	10.53	12.09	80%	88%	85%	84%
Ecuador	16.14	19.56	64%	68%	87%	85%
Egypt	91.51	117.10	40%	41%	99%	95%
El Salvador	6.13	6.41	70%	78%	94%	74%
Equatorial Guinea	0.85	1.24	38%	40%	48%	75%
Eritrea	5.23	7.31	29%	40%	58%	16%
Estonia	1.31	1.24	66%	66%	100%	97%
Ethiopia	99.39	138.30	19%	27%	57%	27%
Fiji	0.89	0.94	54%	59%	96%	91%
Finland	5.50	5.71	84%	85%	100%	98%
France	64.40	68.01	80%	84%	100%	99%
Gabon	1.73	2.32	88%	91%	93%	42%
Gambia	1.99	3.10	59%	65%	90%	59%
Georgia	4.00	3.87	58%	59%	100%	87%
Germany	80.69	79.29	77%	79%	100%	99%
Ghana	27.41	36.87	53%	60%	89%	15%
Greece	10.95	10.48	79%	86%	100%	99%
Grenada	0.11	0.11	36%	36%	97%	98%
Guatemala	16.34	21.42	51%	62%	93%	64%
Guinea	12.61	18.28	36%	43%	77%	20%
Guinea-Bissau	1.84	2.54	48%	57%	79%	21%
Guyana	0.77	0.82	30%	33%	98%	84%
Haiti	10.71	12.58	58%	70%	58%	27%
Honduras	8.08	9.74	57%	69%	91%	83%
Hungary	9.86	9.27	72%	79%	100%	98%
Iceland	0.33	0.36	96%	100%	100%	99%
India	1,311.05	1,527.66	32%	38%	94%	40%
Indonesia	257.56	295.48	53%	63%	87%	61%
Iran	79.11	88.53	74%	82%	96%	90%
Iraq	36.42	54.07	68%	68%	87%	86%
Ireland	4.69	5.20	64%	70%	98%	91%
Israel	8.06	10.00	90%	90%	100%	100%
Italy	59.80	59.10	71%	75%	100%	100%
Jamaica	2.79	2.87	55%	61%	94%	82%
Japan	126.57	120.13	94%	97%	100%	100%
Jordan	7.59	9.11	85%	89%	97%	99%
Kazakhstan	17.63	20.07	51%	52%	93%	98%
Kenya	46.05	65.41	26%	33%	63%	30%
Kiribati	0.11	0.14	42%	44%	67%	40%
Kuwait	3.89	4.99	91%	96%	99%	100%
Kyrgyzstan	5.94	7.10	34%	39%	90%	93%
Laos	6.80	8.49	40%	53%	76%	71%
Latvia	1.97	1.81	69%	71%	99%	87%
Lebanon	5.85	5.29	76%	88%	99%	81%
Lesotho	2.14	2.49	27%	35%	82%	30%
Liberia	4.50	6.41	50%	56%	76%	17%
Libya	6.28	7.42	79%	82%	0%	97%

5 Total renewable water resources m³ per person per year 2014	6 Total renewable water resources million m³ 2014	7 Water dependency % of water originating outside country 2014	8 Annual renewable groundwater million m³ 2014	9 Annual renewable surface water million m³ 2014	
2,778	200	0%	–	0	Dominica
2,232	23,500	0%	23,500	4,161	Dominican Republic
27,679	442,400	0%	432,000	134,000	Ecuador
699	58,300	97%	56,000	2,300	Egypt
4,115	26,270	41%	22,690	6,150	El Salvador
33,419	26,000	0%	25,000	10,000	Equatorial Guinea
1,119	7,315	62%	7,215	500	Eritrea
9,977	12,810	1%	11,810	4,000	Estonia
1,264	122,000	0%	120,000	20,000	Ethiopia
32,187	28,550	0%	28,550	5,273	Fiji
20,209	110,000	3%	109,800	2,200	Finland
3,264	211,000	5%	209,000	120,000	France
97,019	166,000	1%	164,000	62,000	Gabon
4,191	8,000	63%	8,000	500	Gambia
14,650	63,330	8%	62,100	17,230	Georgia
1,863	154,000	31%	153,300	45,700	Germany
2,125	56,200	46%	54,900	26,300	Ghana
6,147	68,400	15%	65,900	10,300	Greece
1,887	200	0%	–	0	Grenada
8,064	127,900	15%	119,400	33,700	Guatemala
18,765	226,000	0%	226,000	38,000	Guinea
17,984	31,400	49%	27,400	14,000	Guinea-Bissau
337,065	271,000	11%	271,000	103,000	Guyana
1,341	14,030	7%	11,870	2,157	Haiti
11,156	92,160	2%	83,070	39,000	Honduras
10,470	104,000	94%	104,000	6,000	Hungary
510,511	170,000	0%	166,000	24,000	Iceland
1,508	1,911,000	31%	1,869,000	432,000	India
7,986	2,019,000	0%	1,973,000	457,400	Indonesia
1,746	137,000	7%	105,800	49,300	Iran
2,584	89,860	61%	88,580	3,280	Iraq
11,118	52,000	6%	51,200	10,800	Ireland
228	1,780	58%	555	1,225	Israel
3,132	191,300	5%	179,300	43,000	Italy
3,866	10,820	0%	9,111	5,472	Jamaica
3,386	430,000	0%	420,000	27,000	Japan
125	937	27%	650	540	Jordan
6,527	108,400	41%	100,600	33,850	Kazakhstan
674	30,700	33%	30,200	3,500	Kenya
–	–	0%	–	0	Kiribati
6	20	100%	–	20	Kuwait
4,199	23,620	1%	21,150	13,690	Kyrgyzstan
48,375	333,500	43%	333,500	37,900	Laos
17,369	35,450	53%	35,250	2,200	Latvia
907	4,503	1%	3,803	3,200	Lebanon
1,440	3,022	0%	3,022	500	Lesotho
52,763	232,000	14%	232,000	45,000	Liberia
112	700	0%	200	600	Libya

	1 Total population millions		2 Urban population as % of total		3 Improved water source % of population with access 2015	4 Improved sanitation % of population with access 2014
	2015	2030 projected	2015	2030 projected		
Lithuania	2.88	2.66	69%	73%	97%	92%
Luxembourg	0.57	0.68	86%	87%	100%	98%
Macedonia	2.08	2.08	58%	61%	99%	91%
Madagascar	24.24	35.96	35%	44%	52%	12%
Malawi	17.22	26.58	16%	20%	90%	41%
Malaysia	30.33	36.11	75%	84%	98%	96%
Maldives	0.36	0.44	45%	56%	99%	98%
Mali	17.60	27.37	37%	48%	77%	24%
Malta	0.42	0.43	98%	99%	100%	100%
Marshall Islands	0.05	0.06	73%	80%	95%	77%
Mauritania	4.07	5.67	60%	67%	58%	40%
Mauritius	1.27	1.31	39%	39%	100%	93%
Mexico	127.02	148.13	78%	80%	96%	85%
Micronesia	0.10	0.12	22%	25%	89%	57%
Moldova	4.07	3.84	38%	39%	88%	76%
Mongolia	2.96	3.52	71%	77%	64%	59%
Montenegro	0.63	0.62	64%	66%	100%	96%
Morocco	34.38	39.79	59%	66%	85%	77%
Mozambique	27.98	41.44	31%	36%	51%	20%
Myanmar	53.90	60.24	34%	42%	81%	80%
Namibia	2.46	3.27	45%	55%	91%	34%
Nauru	0.01	0.01	99%	100%	–	–
Nepal	28.51	33.10	19%	25%	92%	44%
Netherlands	16.92	17.60	90%	93%	100%	98%
New Zealand	4.53	5.10	88%	89%	100%	–
Nicaragua	6.08	7.03	60%	68%	87%	68%
Niger	19.90	35.97	18%	24%	58%	11%
Nigeria	182.20	262.60	48%	61%	69%	29%
North Korea	25.16	26.70	61%	65%	100%	82%
Norway	5.21	5.94	79%	82%	100%	98%
Oman	4.49	5.24	72%	78%	93%	97%
Pakistan	188.92	244.92	39%	44%	91%	62%
Palau	0.02	0.02	87%	92%	95%	100%
Palestine Authority	4.67	6.76	73%	75%	58%	92%
Panama	3.93	4.78	68%	73%	95%	75%
Papua New Guinea	7.62	10.06	13%	15%	40%	19%
Paraguay	6.64	7.84	63%	71%	98%	88%
Peru	31.38	36.86	78%	82%	87%	75%
Philippines	100.70	123.58	45%	48%	92%	73%
Poland	38.61	37.21	60%	63%	98%	97%
Portugal	10.35	9.84	65%	75%	100%	100%
Puerto Rico	3.68	3.64	94%	95%	–	99%
Qatar	2.24	2.78	100%	100%	100%	98%
Romania	19.51	17.64	60%	67%	100%	79%
Russia	143.46	138.65	73%	74%	97%	72%
Rwanda	11.61	15.78	31%	47%	76%	61%
St Kitts and Nevis	0.06	0.06	32%	35%	98%	–
St Lucia	0.19	0.20	18%	20%	96%	91%

5 Total renewable water resources m³ per person per year 2014	6 Total renewable water resources million m³ 2014	7 Water dependency % of water originating outside country 2014	8 Annual renewable groundwater million m³ 2014	9 Annual renewable surface water million m³ 2014	
8,145	24,500	37%	24,400	1,100	Lithuania
6,518	3,500	71%	3,500	80	Luxembourg
3,036	6,400	16%	6,400	0	Macedonia
14,297	337,000	0%	332,000	55,000	Madagascar
1,027	17,280	7%	17,280	2,500	Malawi
19,213	580,000	0%	566,000	64,000	Malaysia
85	30	0%	–	30	Maldives
7,610	120,000	50%	110,000	20,000	Mali
117	51	0%	1	50	Malta
–	–	0%	–	0	Marshall Islands
2,861	11,400	96%	11,100	300	Mauritania
2,203	2,751	0%	2,358	893	Mauritius
3,731	461,900	12%	402,900	150,000	Mexico
–	–	0%	–	0	Micronesia
3,545	12,270	87%	11,970	1,300	Moldova
12,079	34,800	0%	32,700	6,100	Mongolia
–	–	0%	–	0	Montenegro
866	29,000	0%	22,000	10,000	Morocco
8,201	217,100	54%	214,100	17,000	Mozambique
21,743	1,168,000	14%	1,157,000	453,700	Myanmar
16,997	39,910	85%	37,850	2,100	Namibia
–	–	0%	–	10	Nauru
7,475	210,200	6%	210,200	20,000	Nepal
5,416	91,000	88%	91,000	4,500	Netherlands
71,852	327,000	0%	–	0	New Zealand
26,666	164,500	5%	160,900	59,000	Nicaragua
1,837	34,050	90%	31,550	2,500	Niger
1,603	286,200	23%	279,200	87,000	Nigeria
3,083	77,150	13%	76,150	13,000	North Korea
77,180	393,000	3%	387,000	96,000	Norway
357	1,400	0%	1,050	1,300	Oman
1,333	246,800	78%	239,200	55,000	Pakistan
–	–	0%	–	0	Palau
189	837	3%	87	750	Palestine Authority
35,481	139,300	2%	135,900	21,000	Panama
107,143	801,000	0%	801,000	211,600	Papua New Guinea
56,057	387,800	70%	387,800	41,640	Paraguay
61,100	1,880,000	13%	1,880,000	303,000	Peru
4,785	479,000	0%	444,000	180,000	Philippines
1,583	60,500	11%	60,000	12,500	Poland
7,295	77,400	51%	77,400	4,000	Portugal
1,927	7,100	0%	–	0	Puerto Rico
26	58	3%	–	58	Qatar
9,797	212,000	80%	211,500	8,460	Romania
31,762	4,525,000	5%	4,249,000	788,000	Russia
1,099	13,300	29%	13,300	7,000	Rwanda
436	24	0%	4	20	St Kitts and Nevis
1,630	300	0%	–	0	St Lucia

NEEDS AND RESOURCES

	1 Total population millions		2 Urban population as % of total		3 Improved water source % of population with access 2015	4 Improved sanitation % of popula... with acce... 2014
	2015	2030 projected	2015	2030 projected		
St Vincent and the Grenadines	0.11	0.11	51%	55%	95%	–
Samoa	0.19	0.21	19%	19%	99%	92%
São Tome and Principe	0.19	0.26	69%	77%	97%	35%
Saudi Arabia	31.54	39.13	79%	78%	97%	100%
Senegal	15.13	22.80	43%	48%	79%	47%
Serbia	8.85	8.28	59%	61%	99%	97%
Seychelles	0.10	0.10	52%	57%	96%	98%
Sierra Leone	6.45	8.60	39%	44%	63%	13%
Singapore	5.60	6.42	100%	100%	100%	100%
Slovakia	5.43	5.35	54%	55%	100%	99%
Slovenia	2.07	2.05	50%	53%	100%	99%
Solomon Islands	0.58	0.76	22%	29%	81%	30%
Somalia	10.79	16.49	41%	48%	32%	–
South Africa	54.49	60.03	64%	69%	93%	66%
South Korea	50.29	52.52	82%	84%	98%	100%
South Sudan	12.34	17.81	19%	23%	59%	7%
Spain	46.12	45.92	81%	87%	100%	100%
Sri Lanka	20.72	21.54	19%	23%	96%	95%
Sudan	40.23	56.44	33%	38%	0%	24%
Suriname	0.54	0.60	67%	67%	95%	79%
Swaziland	1.29	1.51	21%	23%	74%	58%
Sweden	9.78	10.77	85%	87%	100%	99%
Switzerland	8.30	9.22	73%	78%	100%	100%
Syria	18.50	28.65	69%	67%	90%	96%
Tajikistan	8.48	11.10	27%	31%	74%	95%
Tanzania	53.47	82.93	31%	40%	56%	15%
Thailand	67.96	68.25	50%	63%	98%	93%
Timor-Leste	1.18	1.58	32%	40%	72%	40%
Togo	7.30	10.49	39%	46%	63%	12%
Tonga	0.11	0.12	24%	26%	100%	91%
Trinidad and Tobago	1.36	1.37	8%	8%	95%	92%
Tunisia	11.25	12.69	67%	70%	98%	92%
Turkey	78.67	87.72	72%	78%	100%	95%
Turkmenistan	5.37	6.16	50%	56%	–	–
Tuvalu	0.01	0.01	60%	70%	98%	–
Uganda	39.03	61.93	17%	23%	79%	19%
Ukraine	44.82	40.89	69%	72%	96%	96%
United Arab Emirates	9.16	10.98	89%	99%	100%	98%
United Kingdom	64.72	70.11	81%	84%	100%	99%
United States of America	321.77	355.76	82%	86%	99%	100%
Uruguay	3.43	3.60	95%	96%	100%	96%
Uzbekistan	29.89	34.40	36%	41%	87%	100%
Vanuatu	0.26	0.35	26%	31%	95%	58%
Venezuela	31.11	36.67	90%	91%	93%	94%
Vietnam	93.45	105.22	34%	42%	98%	76%
Yemen	26.83	36.34	33%	40%	55%	–
Zambia	16.21	25.31	39%	48%	65%	44%
Zimbabwe	15.60	21.35	31%	32%	77%	37%

5 Total renewable water resources m³ per person per year 2014	6 Total renewable water resources million m³ 2014	7 Water dependency % of water originating outside country 2014	8 Annual renewable groundwater million m³ 2014	9 Annual renewable surface water million m³ 2014	
917	100	0%	–	0	St Vincent and the Grenadines
–	–	0%	–	0	Samoa
11,010	2,180	0%	–	0	São Tomé and Principe
82	2,400	0%	2,200	2,200	Saudi Arabia
2,679	38,970	34%	36,970	3,500	Senegal
17,131	162,200	0%	–	0	Serbia
–	–	0%	–	0	Seychelles
25,786	160,000	0%	150,000	25,000	Sierra Leone
109	600	0%	–	0	Singapore
9,186	50,100	75%	50,100	1,730	Slovakia
15,352	31,870	41%	31,720	13,500	Slovenia
78,010	44,700	0%	44,700	11,920	Solomon Islands
1,360	14,700	59%	14,400	3,300	Somalia
966	51,350	13%	49,550	4,800	South Africa
1,408	69,700	7%	67,100	13,300	South Korea
4,217	49,500	66%	49,500	4,000	South Sudan
2,369	111,500	0%	109,800	29,900	Spain
2,462	52,800	0%	52,000	7,800	Sri Lanka
975	37,800	96%	35,800	3,000	Sudan
181,985	99,000	0%	99,000	90,000	Suriname
3,557	4,510	41%	4,510	660	Swaziland
18,067	174,000	2%	173,000	20,000	Sweden
6,558	53,500	24%	53,500	2,500	Switzerland
764	16,800	72%	12,630	6,174	Syria
2,606	21,910	17%	18,910	6,000	Tajikistan
1,897	96,270	13%	92,270	30,000	Tanzania
6,525	438,600	49%	427,400	41,900	Thailand
7,131	8,215	0%	8,129	886	Timor-Leste
2,102	14,700	22%	14,000	5,700	Togo
–	–	0%	–	0	Tonga
2,857	3,840	0%	3,740	614	Trinidad and Tobago
415	4,615	9%	3,420	1,595	Tunisia
2,790	211,600	2%	171,800	67,800	Turkey
4,667	24,770	97%	24,360	405	Turkmenistan
–	–	0%	–	0	Tuvalu
1,547	60,100	35%	60,100	29,000	Uganda
3,901	175,300	69%	170,300	22,000	Ukraine
16	150	0%	150	120	United Arab Emirates
2,306	147,000	1%	146,200	9,800	United Kingdom
9,514	3,069,000	8%	2,913,000	1,383,000	United States of America
50,366	172,200	46%	172,200	22,900	Uruguay
1,666	48,870	80%	42,070	8,800	Uzbekistan
–	–	0%	–	4,377	Vanuatu
42,948	1,325,000	39%	1,303,000	227,000	Venezuela
9,553	884,100	59%	847,700	71,420	Vietnam
84	2,100	0%	2,000	1,500	Yemen
6,977	104,800	23%	104,800	47,000	Zambia
1,370	20,000	39%	19,000	6,000	Zimbabwe

WATER USES

	1 Total water use m³ per person 2013 or latest available	2 Water use per sector					
		m³ per person 2013 or latest available			As % of total 2013 or latest available		
		Agriculture	Industry	Municipal	Agriculture	Industry	Muni
Afghanistan	913	901	6	7	99%	1%	1
Albania	414	163	73	177	39%	18%	43
Algeria	219	130	11	78	59%	5%	36
Angola	40	8	14	18	21%	34%	45
Antigua and Barbuda	129	20	28	81	16%	22%	63
Argentina	920	680	97	142	74%	11%	15
Armenia	991	388	43	292	39%	4%	30
Australia	836	549	107	180	66%	13%	22
Austria	452	12	357	83	3%	79%	18
Azerbaijan	1,286	1085	249	55	84%	19%	4
Bahamas	–		–	0	0%	0%	0
Bahrain	346	154	20	172	45%	6%	50
Bangladesh	232	204	5	23	88%	2%	10
Barbados	294	199	22	72	68%	8%	25
Belarus	163	53	51	59	32%	32%	36
Belgium	558	4	491	64	1%	88%	11
Belize	401	271	84	45	68%	21%	11
Benin	18	8	4	6	45%	23%	32
Bhutan	456	429	4	23	94%	1%	5
Bolivia	199	183	3	13	92%	2%	7
Bosnia and Herzegovina	86	0	13	0	0%	15%	0
Botswana	107	44	19	44	41%	18%	41
Brazil	377	226	64	87	60%	17%	23
Brunei Darussalam	–		–	0	0%	0%	0
Bulgaria	841	137	570	134	16%	68%	16
Burkina Faso	57	30	2	26	51%	3%	46
Burundi	41	32	2	7	77%	6%	17
Cambodia	159	149	2	7	94%	2%	4
Cameroon	58	44	4	10	76%	7%	17
Canada	1,114	136	893	159	12%	80%	14
Cape Verde	48	44	1	3	91%	2%	7
Central African Republic	18	0	3	15	1%	17%	83
Chad	82	63	10	10	76%	12%	12
Chile	2,126	1765	285	76	83%	13%	4
China	406	262	94	49	65%	23%	12
Colombia	247	134	47	66	54%	19%	27
Comoros	18	8	1	9	47%	5%	48
Congo	14	1	3	10	9%	22%	70
Congo, Dem Rep	12	1	3	8	11%	21%	68
Costa Rica	476	269	53	154	57%	11%	32
Côte d'Ivoire	86	33	18	35	38%	21%	41
Croatia	146	2	20	124	1%	14%	85
Cuba	618	401	66	151	65%	11%	24
Cyprus	163	141	5	17	86%	3%	10
Czech Republic	173	4	109	60	2%	63%	35
Denmark	117	29	23	64	25%	20%	55
Djibouti	26	4	0	22	16%	0%	84

3 Water Footprint m³ per person consumed directly, embedded, made unusable 5 or latest available	4 Irrigation Area equipped as % of total cultivated area 2013 or latest available	5 Hydropower As a % of total electricity produced 2013 or latest available	6 Aquaculture Tonnes of fish, crustaceans and molluscs produced 2013	7 Wetlands of International Importance km² 2015	
–	41%	–	1,050	–	Afghanistan
1,555	48%	100%	2,090	982	Albania
1,589	15%	1%	2,193	29,910	Algeria
958	2%	71%	450	–	Angola
1,568	8%	–	–	–	Antigua and Barbuda
1,607	6%	22%	3,825	53,823	Argentina
1,439	54%	29%	11,590	4,935	Armenia
2,315	6%	7%	76,062	83,202	Australia
1,598	8%	65%	3,237	1,250	Austria
1,245	67%	8%	325	996	Azerbaijan
2,133	8%	0%	–	–	Bahamas
–	78%	0%	–	68	Bahrain
769	59%	2%	1,859,808	6,112	Bangladesh
2,090	39%	–	–	–	Barbados
1,718	1%	0%	13,548	6,147	Belarus
1,888	3%	0%	212	470	Belgium
2,010	3%	–	7,140	236	Belize
1,136	1%	0%	667	11,794	Benin
–	28%	0%	70	3	Bhutan
3,468	6%	31%	1,076	148,424	Bolivia
1,256	0%	30%	2,924	568	Bosnia and Herzegovina
2,051	1%	0%	–	55,374	Botswana
2,027	7%	75%	473,429	72,257	Brazil
3,421	0%	0%	830	–	Brunei Darussalam
2,297	3%	7%	12,152	499	Bulgaria
1,703	1%	–	200	6,525	Burkina Faso
719	2%	–	165	785	Burundi
1,078	9%	36%	90,000	546	Cambodia
1,245	0%	72%	840	8,271	Cameroon
2,333	2%	60%	172,097	130,868	Canada
1,244	7%	–	–	–	Cape Verde
1,193	0%	–	140	3,763	Central African Republic
1,462	1%	–	–	124,051	Chad
1,155	64%	27%	1,033,206	3,618	Chile
1,071	51%	17%	43,549,738	40,022	China
1,375	31%	76%	89,398	7,087	Colombia
1,325	0%	–	–	–	Comoros
786	0%	61%	119	135,076	Congo
552	0%	100%	2,869	74,356	Congo, Dem Rep
1,490	18%	71%	30,174	5,697	Costa Rica
1,295	0%	25%	3,720	1,273	Côte d'Ivoire
1,688	2%	45%	12,019	944	Croatia
1,687	16%	1%	29,578	11,884	Cuba
2,385	38%	0%	5,340	11	Cyprus
1,651	1%	3%	19,357	602	Czech Republic
1,635	19%	0%	107,519	23,154	Denmark
–	0%	0%	–	30	Djibouti

Water Uses

	1 Total water use m³ per person 2013 or latest available	2 Water use per sector					
		m³ per person 2013 or latest available			As % of total 2013 or latest available		
		Agriculture	Industry	Municipal	Agriculture	Industry	Munic
Dominica	278	14	0	264	5%	0%	95
Dominican Republic	696	556	57	83	80%	8%	12
Ecuador	695	566	38	91	81%	6%	13
Egypt	1,000	864	59	78	86%	6%	8
El Salvador	346	234	35	77	68%	10%	22
Equatorial Guinea	32	2	5	25	6%	15%	79
Eritrea	112	106	0	6	95%	0%	5
Estonia	1,263	3	1212	48	0%	96%	4
Ethiopia	79	74	0	5	94%	0%	6
Fiji	100	61	11	28	61%	11%	28
Finland	1,240	9	1153	77	1%	93%	6
France	518	49	383	86	9%	74%	17
Gabon	96	28	10	59	29%	10%	61
Gambia	69	30	13	26	43%	19%	37
Georgia	418	243	92	83	58%	22%	20
Germany	399	3	335	61	1%	84%	15
Ghana	50	33	5	12	66%	10%	24
Greece	862	764	21	76	89%	2%	9
Grenada	133	20	0	113	15%	0%	85
Guatemala	250	142	45	63	57%	18%	25
Guinea	61	32	6	23	53%	9%	38
Guinea-Bissau	132	108	6	17	82%	5%	13
Guyana	1,818	1715	26	77	94%	1%	4
Haiti	143	119	5	19	83%	4%	13
Honduras	224	164	16	44	73%	7%	20%
Hungary	506	32	402	72	6%	79%	14%
Iceland	541	229	46	266	42%	8%	49%
India	615	556	14	45	90%	2%	7%
Indonesia	527	431	34	61	82%	7%	12%
Iran	1,299	1197	15	86	92%	1%	7%
Iraq	2,615	2060	384	170	79%	15%	7%
Ireland	165	0	12	137	0%	7%	83%
Israel	282	163	16	103	58%	6%	36%
Italy	883	389	317	149	44%	36%	17%
Jamaica	300	165	28	106	55%	9%	35%
Japan	640	428	91	121	67%	14%	19%
Jordan	166	108	7	52	65%	4%	31%
Kazakhstan	1,299	860	385	54	66%	30%	4%
Kenya	75	44	3	27	59%	4%	37%
Kiribati	–		–	0	0%	0%	0%
Kuwait	446	240	10	196	54%	2%	44%
Kyrgyzstan	1,560	1451	65	44	93%	4%	3%
Laos	581	531	28	22	91%	5%	4%
Latvia	180	23	88	69	13%	49%	38%
Lebanon	316	188	36	92	60%	11%	29%
Lesotho	23	2	11	11	9%	46%	46%
Liberia	43	4	15	23	9%	36%	54%

3 Water Footprint m³ per person consumed directly, embedded, made unusable 5 or latest available	4 Irrigation Area equipped as % of total cultivated area 2013 or latest available	5 Hydropower As a % of total electricity produced 2013 or latest available	6 Aquaculture Tonnes of fish, crustaceans and molluscs produced 2013	7 Wetlands of International Importance km² 2015	
2,716	1%	0%	–	1,351	Dominica
1,401	27%	11%	1,020	–	Dominican Republic
2,007	59%	54%	332,180	2,867	Ecuador
1,341	100%	8%	1,097,544	4,155	Egypt
1,032	5%	31%	3,278	2,074	El Salvador
–	0%	–	15	1,360	Equatorial Guinea
1,089	0%	0%	–	–	Eritrea
1,720	0%	0%	733	3,048	Estonia
1,167	3%	99%	45	–	Ethiopia
1,767	2%	–	202	6	Fiji
1,414	3%	18%	13,613	7,995	Finland
1,786	14%	13%	201,860	35,578	France
1,451	0%	41%	160	28,185	Gabon
887	1%	–	33	312	Gambia
2,267	75%	75%	650	345	Georgia
1,426	4%	3%	25,289	8,682	Germany
1,207	0%	67%	32,513	1,761	Ghana
2,338	42%	11%	144,595	1,635	Greece
2,154	4%	–	–	–	Grenada
983	16%	47%	17,047	6,286	Guatemala
1,606	3%	0%	250	64,224	Guinea
1,198	0%	0%	–	11,896	Guinea-Bissau
1,548	32%	14%	221	–	Guyana
1,030	8%	37%	720	–	Haiti
1,177	6%	1%	70,427	2,702	Honduras
2,384	3%	71%	14,918	2,449	Hungary
2,109	0%	11%	7,052	1,287	Iceland
1,089	39%	7%	4,549,607	6,891	India
1,124	16%	5%	3,819,732	13,730	Indonesia
1,866	52%	9%	325,325	14,864	Iran
–	0%	2%	14,060	5,379	Iraq
1,301	0%	0%	34,157	670	Ireland
2,303	59%	18%	22,141	4	Israel
2,303	41%	4%	162,620	602	Italy
1,696	14%	7%	836	378	Jamaica
1,379	55%	0%	608,800	1,480	Japan
1,678	38%	8%	600	74	Jordan
2,376	7%	52%	811	32,814	Kazakhstan
1,101	2%	70%	23,501	2,654	Kenya
2,859	–	–	–	–	Kiribati
2,072	68%	93%	301	509	Kuwait
1,499	76%	60%	300	6,794	Kyrgyzstan
1,041	23%	0%	108,000	–	Laos
1,797	0%	7%	643	1,503	Latvia
2,112	0%	0%	1,280	11	Lebanon
1,640	0%	–	500	4	Lesotho
1,235	0%	–	30	959	Liberia

WATER USES

	1 Total water use m³ per person 2013 or latest available	2 Water use per sector					
		m³ per person 2013 or latest available			As % of total 2013 or latest available		
		Agriculture	Industry	Municipal	Agriculture	Industry	Munic
Libya	810	671	25	114	83%	3%	14
Lithuania	746	26	671	49	3%	90%	7
Luxembourg	86	0	7	78	0%	8%	91
Macedonia	490	60	327	103	12%	67%	21
Madagascar	986	964	8	14	98%	1%	1
Malawi	99	85	3	10	86%	4%	11
Malaysia	418	93	179	146	22%	43%	35
Maldives	17	0	1	17	0%	5%	95
Mali	408	399	0	8	98%	0%	2
Malta	132	46	1	84	35%	1%	64
Marshall Islands	–		–	0	0%	0%	0
Mauritania	405	367	10	29	91%	2%	7
Mauritius	594	402	16	175	68%	3%	30
Mexico	665	510	60	95	77%	9%	14
Micronesia	–	0	0	0	0%	0%	0
Moldova	290	10	240	40	3%	83%	14
Mongolia	197	87	85	25	44%	43%	13
Montenegro	259	3	101	155	1%	39%	60
Morocco	321	282	7	33	88%	2%	10
Mozambique	46	36	1	9	78%	3%	19
Myanmar	675	600	7	67	89%	1%	10
Namibia	147	103	7	37	70%	5%	25
Nepal	366	359	1	6	98%	0%	2
Netherlands	638	7	558	73	1%	87%	11
New Zealand	1,166	719	265	182	62%	23%	16
Nicaragua	258	198	12	48	77%	5%	19
Niger	69	46	2	21	67%	3%	30
Nigeria	89	48	13	28	54%	15%	31
North Korea	359	274	47	37	76%	13%	10
Norway	623	179	267	176	29%	43%	28
Oman	514	454	7	52	88%	1%	10
Pakistan	1,024	962	8	54	94%	1%	5
Palestine Authority	112	51	8	54	45%	7%	48
Panama	273	117	3	153	43%	1%	56
Papua New Guinea	61	0	26	35	0%	43%	57
Paraguay	361	284	23	54	79%	6%	15
Peru	456	404	10	42	89%	2%	9
Philippines	843	694	85	64	82%	10%	8
Poland	300	29	218	53	10%	73%	18
Portugal	867	0	0	92	0%	0%	11
Puerto Rico	266	20	5	242	7%	2%	91
Qatar	385	227	7	151	59%	2%	39
Romania	316	54	193	69	17%	61%	22
Russia	455	91	272	92	20%	60%	20
Rwanda	17	11	1	4	68%	8%	24
St Kitts and Nevis	289	4	–	285	1%	0%	99
St Lucia	252	179	–	74	71%	0%	29

3 Water Footprint m³ per person consumed directly, embedded, made unusable 05 or latest available	4 Irrigation Area equipped as % of total cultivated area 2013 or latest available	5 Hydropower As a % of total electricity produced 2013 or latest available	6 Aquaculture Tonnes of fish, crustaceans and molluscs produced 2013	7 Wetlands of International Importance km² 2015	
2,038	22%	9%	10	1	Libya
1,516	0%	6%	4,211	656	Lithuania
2,514	0%	17%	–	172	Luxembourg
1,348	27%	7%	1,340	216	Macedonia
1,576	31%	–	8,974	13,476	Madagascar
936	2%	–	3,705	2,248	Malawi
2,103	5%	0%	261,274	1,342	Malaysia
1,361	–	–	–	–	Maldives
2,044	5%	–	2,205	42,046	Mali
2,216	34%	3%	3,939	42,046	Malta
–	–	–	–	–	Marshall Islands
2,565	11%	–	–	12,406	Mauritania
2,161	23%	9%	485	–	Mauritius
1,978	25%	5%	168,792	86,436	Mexico
–	–	–	–	–	Micronesia
1,327	11%	0%	9,520	947	Moldova
3,775	0%	52%	–	14,395	Mongolia
–	1%	6%	811	202	Montenegro
1,725	16%	100%	1,768	2,720	Morocco
1,119	3%	72%	721	20,517	Mozambique
1,217	18%	98%	929,180	104	Myanmar
1,682	1%	99%	470	6,766	Namibia
1,201	48%	0%	36,020	345	Nepal
1,466	42%	54%	60,410	9,039	Netherlands
1,589	124%	10%	97,123	555	New Zealand
912	11%	20%	26,407	4,069	Nicaragua
3,519	1%	–	200	43,179	Niger
1,242	1%	13%	278,706	10,767	Nigeria
888	0%	1%	64,050	–	North Korea
1,423	13%	0%	1,247,865	8,895	Norway
–	91%	31%	353	1	Oman
1,331	64%	63%	148,120	13,436	Pakistan
1,055	12%	–	284	–	Palestine Authority
1,364	4%	100%	8,335	1,840	Panama
–	–	–	2,025	5,949	Papua New Guinea
1,954	3%	54%	5,700	7,860	Paraguay
1,088	47%	14%	125,649	67,840	Peru
1,378	18%	1%	815,008	1,544	Philippines
1,405	1%	27%	35,208	1,451	Poland
2,505	31%	0%	7,889	1,325	Portugal
–	22%	–	–	–	Puerto Rico
–	89%	21%	56	–	Qatar
1,689	7%	16%	11,007	11,564	Romania
1,852	2%	0%	154,898	103,238	Russia
821	1%	–	1,175	–	Rwanda
1,632	0%	–	–	–	St Kitts and Nevis
1,559	32%	–	–	–	St Lucia

WATER USES

	1 Total water use m³ per person 2013 or latest available	2 Water use per sector					
		m³ per person 2013 or latest available			As % of total 2013 or latest available		
		Agriculture	Industry	Municipal	Agriculture	Industry	Munic
St Vincent and the Grenadines	78	0	0	78	0%	0%	100
Samoa	–	–	–	0	0%	0%	0
São Tome and Principe	–	–	–	0	0%	0%	0
Saudi Arabia	913	804	27	82	88%	3%	9
Senegal	214	199	6	9	93%	3%	4
Serbia	431	8	352	71	2%	82%	17
Seychelles	154	10	43	101	7%	28%	66
Sierra Leone	39	8	10	20	22%	26%	52
Singapore	–	–	–	0	0%	0%	0
Slovakia	127	4	64	59	3%	50%	47
Slovenia	452	1	369	82	0%	82%	18
Solomon Islands	–	–	–	0	0%	0%	0
Somalia	370	368	0	2	99%	0%	0
South Africa	271	170	16	85	63%	6%	31
South Korea	614	336	94	146	55%	15%	24
South Sudan	61	22	21	18	36%	34%	29
Spain	717	456	147	114	64%	21%	16
Sri Lanka	638	557	41	40	87%	6%	6
Sudan	724	697	2	26	96%	0%	4%
Suriname	1,208	846	266	97	70%	22%	8%
Swaziland	963	930	11	22	97%	1%	2%
Sweden	283	10	177	95	4%	63%	34%
Switzerland	248	25	133	90	10%	54%	36%
Syria	857	750	31	75	88%	4%	9%
Tajikistan	1,616	1468	57	91	91%	4%	6%
Tanzania	145	129	1	15	89%	0%	10%
Thailand	867	784	42	41	90%	5%	5%
Timor-Leste	1,131	1034	2	96	91%	0%	8%
Togo	33	15	1	17	45%	2%	53%
Trinidad and Tobago	287	12	96	178	4%	34%	62%
Tunisia	304	243	15	46	80%	5%	15%
Turkey	577	426	62	89	74%	11%	15%
Turkmenistan	5,753	5426	173	155	94%	3%	3%
Uganda	18	7	1	9	41%	8%	51%
Ukraine	326	98	157	72	30%	48%	22%
United Arab Emirates	690	571	12	106	83%	2%	15%
United Kingdom	172	16	56	100	9%	32%	58%
United States of America	1,575	633	726	215	40%	46%	14%
Uruguay	1,100	953	24	123	87%	2%	11%
Uzbekistan	2,100	1890	56	154	90%	3%	7%
Vanuatu	–	–	–	0	0%	0%	0%
Venezuela	818	604	29	185	74%	4%	23%
Vietnam	948	898	36	14	95%	4%	1%
Yemen	168	153	3	13	91%	2%	7%
Zambia	148	108	12	27	73%	8%	18%
Zimbabwe	280	230	17	33	82%	6%	12%

3 Water Footprint m³ per person consumed directly, embedded, made unusable [0]5 or latest available	4 Irrigation Area equipped as % of total cultivated area 2013 or latest available	5 Hydropower As a % of total electricity produced 2013 or latest available	6 Aquaculture Tonnes of fish, crustaceans and molluscs produced 2013	7 Wetlands of International Importance km² 2015	
1,689	6%	–	–	–	St Vincent and the Grenadines
2,082	0%	–	–	–	Samoa
1,728	0%	–	–	–	São Tomé and Principe
1,849	44%	8%	25,402	–	Saudi Arabia
1,151	4%	26%	705	1,000	Senegal
2,390	3%	0%	5,936	639	Serbia
2,192	9%	–	–	–	Seychelles
1,438	–	–	80	2,950	Sierra Leone
–	–	17%	5,165	–	Singapore
1,335	12%	29%	1,085	407	Slovakia
2,012	4%	1%	1,226	82	Slovenia
723	–	–	2	–	Solomon Islands
–	19%	–	–	–	Somalia
1,255	13%	13%	4,010	5,557	South Africa
1,629	47%	2%	402,141	186	South Korea
–	1%	–	20	57,000	South Sudan
2,461	20%	28%	223,707	3,031	Spain
1,256	29%	70%	30,856	1,982	Sri Lanka
1,736	9%	40%	1,980	24,896	Sudan
1,347	100%	–	179	120	Suriname
1,398	26%	–	100	–	Swaziland
1,428	6%	56%	13,366	6,517	Sweden
1,528	14%	10%	1,393	147	Switzerland
2,107	23%	100%	4,000	100	Syria
2,387	74%	29%	404	946	Tajikistan
1,026	2%	5%	3,477	48,684	Tanzania
1,407	34%	80%	1,056,944	3,997	Thailand
1,863	16%	–	56	–	Timor-Leste
990	0%	0%	20	12,104	Togo
1,716	15%	1%	–	–	Trinidad and Tobago
2,217	9%	25%	12,184	8,404	Tunisia
1,642	22%	0%	233,864	1,845	Turkey
2,274	95%	5%	30	2,671	Turkmenistan
1,079	0%	–	98,063	4,543	Uganda
1,575	6%	0%	23,175	7,447	Ukraine
3,136	120%	1%	780	203	United Arab Emirates
1,258	4%	6%	194,630	12,789	United Kingdom
2,842	16%	51%	441,098	18,608	United States of America
2,133	11%	21%	217	4,358	Uruguay
1,278	90%	65%	6,900	5,584	Uzbekistan
1,431	–	–	382	–	Vanuatu
1,710	31%	43%	26,580	–	Venezuela
1,058	49%	0%	3,207,200	1,178	Vietnam
901	42%	100%	–	6	Yemen
921	6%	59%	20,271	40,305	Zambia
1,210	4%	0%	10,090	–	Zimbabwe

Sources

For sources available on the internet, in order to avoid urls becoming outdated, only the root address has been given. To view the source, it is recommended that the reader enters the title of the page or document into a search engine.

Part 1 A Finite Resource

1 Global Water
THE WORLD'S WATER
J Linton. What is Water? The history of a modern abstraction. Vancouver: UBC Press, 2010.
I Shikolomanov. World water resources at the beginning of the 21st century. http://webworld.unesco.org [accessed Nov 2015].
UNEP Vital Water Graphics. 5 and 15. www.grida.no/graphicslib/tag/freshwater
World Water Assessment Programme (WWAP): The United Nations World Water Development Report 2: Water – A shared responsibility. UNESCO and Berghahn Books. 2006. Chap 4.

2 Water's Unequal Distribution
1.2 billion people...
United Nations World Water Assessment Programme (WWAP). World Water Development Report: Water for a sustainable world. vol 1. UNESCO, 2015. p 19, citing FAO 2007.
CHINA AND INDIA
FAO Aquastat. www.fao.org [accessed Oct 2015].
UN Population Division. World Population Prospects 2015 [accessed Oct 2015].
South–North Water Transfer Project. www.internationalrivers.org
ARIDITY ZONES
Africa
The DRC National Plan of Elimination of Cholera 2013–2017 is now available. The African Cholera Surveillance Network, 16 April 2013. www.africhol.org
Australia
Australian Water Association. Australia water statistics. www.awa.asn.au
Brazil
R Clarke and J King. O Atlas da Agua. Sao Paolo: Publifolha, 2005. p.95.
North America
Las Vegas. 1972–2013. https://svs.gsfc.nasa.gov
S Goldenberg. Nevada bets on desert water pipeline as Nevada drinks itself dry. The Guardian, 22 March 2012. www.theguardian.com

3 Water Shortage
BC Howard. Mighty rivers run dry from overuse, National Geographic [accessed October 2015]. www.nationalgeographic.com
Charting our water future: Economic frameworks to inform decision-making. The 2030 Water Resources Group, 2009. www.mckinsey.com
SHORTAGES EXPECTED
Freshwater. Supply concerns continue, and uncertainties complicate planning. United States Government Accountability Office. Report to Congressional Requesters. GAO-14-430. May 2014. www.gao.gov
By 2025 4 billion people…
World Economic forum briefing. 2030 Water Resources Group, 2011. p16. www.2030wrg.org
POPULATION AND WATER
FAO Aqwww.fao.org [downloaded Oct 2015].
China Statistical Yearbook 2014. Beijing: China Press. 2015.
Water stress in countries supplied from Himalayan sources
FAO Aquastat. www.fao.org [downloaded Oct 2015].
S Kaushal. What does being "water stressed" mean for India and her neighbours? India waterportal. 10 Sept 2015. www.indiawaterportal.org

4 Rising Demand
1900: 350 cubic metres
I Shiklomanov World water resources at the beginning of the 21st century. http://webworld.unesco.org [accessed Nov 2015].
HOW WATER IS USED; WORLD WATER USE
FAO Aquastat. www.fao.org [downloaded Oct 2015].
INCREASING USE
I Shikolomanov. op cit [accessed Feb 2016].

5 Dwindling Supply
FAO. The irrigation challenge. Issues paper 4. Rome: FAO, 2003. www.fao.org
S Postel. India's food security threatened by groundwater depletion. National Geographic. 3 Feb 2015. www.nationalgeographic.com
T Shar. Groundwater: A global assessment of scale and significance. Chap 10 in: Comprehensive Assessment of Water Management in Agriculture. Colombo: International Water Management Institute and London: Earthscan, 2007. p399.
KA Voss. Groundwater depletion in the Middle East from GRACE with implications for transboundary water management in the Tigris-Euphrates-Western Iran region. Water Resources Research. vol 49(2), Feb 2013. pp904–14.
IS Zekster, LG Everett. Groundwater resources of the world and their use. IHP-VI series on groundwater, no 6. UNESCO, 2004. www.unesco.org
1.5 billion...
Bundesanstalt fur Geowissenschaften under Rohstoffe (BGR). Groundwater. www.bgr.bund.de [accessed October 2015].
982 cubic kilometres
Facts about groundwater. National Ground Water Association. August 2015. www.ngwa.org
GROUNDWATER
WHYMAP. BGR Hannover / UNESCO Paris 2006
Trends in groundwater storage from NASA GRACE Mission (2013–13). www.nasa.gov
Denver, Colorado, USA
Citizen's Guide to Denver Basin Groundwater. Colorado Foundation for Water Education. 2007. www.dcwater.org
Great Plains, USA
M Wines. Wells dry, fertile plains turn to dust, The New York Times, 19 May 2013. www.nytimes.com
An underground pool drying up. NASA map of High Plains aquifer. www.nytimes.com/interactive/
Central Valley Aquifer, California
B Boxall. Overpumping of Central Valley groundwater creating a crisis. Los Angeles Times. 18 March 2015. www.latimes.com
Mexico City, Mexico
Mexico City subsidence. Copernicus data (2014)/ESA/DLR Microwave and Radar Institute–SEOM InSARap study. 11 Dec 2014. www.esa.int
Libya
A al-Khamisi. Severe water crisis looming in Libya. al-Araby, 20 March 2015. www.alaraby.co.uk
Yemen
Yemen: Time running out for solution to water crisis. IRIN, 13 Aug 2012.
K Mahr. What if Yemen is the first country to run out of water? TIME Magazine, 14 Dec 2010.

G Lichtenthäler. Water conflict and cooperation in Yemen. MER 254. Middle East Research and Information Project, Spring 2010. merip.org

Iran

L Brown. Aquifer depletion. The Encyclopedia of Earth. 21 Nov 2013.

North China Plain

Beijing

All dried up. The Economist, 12 Oct 2013. www.economist.com

NW India and Pakistan

Groundwater depletion in India worst in world: NASA. Deccan Herald, 18 June 2015.

S Postel. India's food security threatened by groundwater depletion. National Geographic, 3 Feb 2015.

6 Competition and Conflict

Around 260 river basins...

A Jägerskog, D Phillips. Managing trans-boundary waters for human development. Human Development Report Office. Occasional paper, 2006/9.

WATER DEPENDENCY

FAO Aquastat. www.fao.org [downloaded 21 Oct 2015].

Nile Basin

Nile Basin www.nilebasin.org

ISIL in Iraq

A Milner. Mosul Dam: Why the battle for water matters in Iraq. BBC News. 18 August 2014. www.bbc.co.uk

D Pipes. The acute danger of Iraqi Dams. 1 July 2014 – 20 Dec 2014, citing a number of sources. www.danielpipes.org

Isis captures Iraqi dam, floods areas. al-Akhbar, 11 April 2014. http://english.al-akhbar.com

Kaveri River, India

Inter State Water Disputes in India. Case study – Cauvery River water sharing dispute. 6 Oct 2013. https://interstatedisputes.wordpress.com

Cauvery issue – Timeline. The Hindu, 14 June 2013. www.thehindu.com

Bolivia–Chile

BM Mulligan and GE Eckstein. The Silala/Siloli watershed in Bolivia/Chile: Lessons from the most vulnerable basin in South America. International Conference "Transboundary Aquifers: Challenges and New Directions". ISARM, 2010 www.siagua.org

Central Asia

M Synnott. Sins of the Aral Sea. National Geographic, June 2015. www.nationalgeographic.com

Inernational Crisis Group. Water pressures in Central Asia. Europe and Central Asia

Report no. 233. 11 September 2014. www.crisisgroup.org

Pacific Institute. Water Conflict Chronology Map. www2.worldwater.org/conflict/map/

7 Environmental Security

Millennium Ecosystem Assessment. Ecosystems and Human Well-being: Wetlands and water. World Resources Institute, 2005. www.millenniumassessment.org

Just over 2 million...

Ramsar Convention. www.ramsar.org

PROTECTED WETLANDS

Ramsar Convention. [accessed Nov 2016].

Florida Everglades

D Raines Ward. Water Wars: Drought, flood, folly and the politics of thirst. Riverhead Books, 2002.

M Grunwald. Sweet deal. Time, 7 July 2008. www.time.com

WM Williams. Florida deal for Everglades may help big sugar. New York Times, 13 Sept 2008. www.nytimes.com

Reconnecting lakes in the Yangtze basin

World Water Assessment Programme (WWAP). The United Nations World Water Development Report 2015: Water for a sustainable world. vol 1. UNESCO, 2015. p28. www.unesco-ihe.org

Tonle Sap, Cambodia

Millennium Ecosystem Assessment. op cit. p30.

F Pearce. Where have all the fish gone? The mighty Mekong is drying up - and so is the river's rich harvest. Vast new dams in China could be to blame. 21 April 2004. www.mongabay.com

P Navarro. Quake lakes spur rethinking of China's dam building strategy. China Brief. vol 8 (12), 6 June 2008. Jamestown Foundation. www.jamestown.org

Inner Niger Delta, Mali

Inner Niger Delta flooded savannah. Encyclopedia of Earth, 2 Sept 2008. www.eoearth.org

RECOVERING THE GARDEN OF EDEN

Nature Iraq. www.natureiraq.org

E Gies. Restoring Iraq's Garden of Eden. New York Times, 17 April 2013.

Le projet "Eden Again" en Irak. 19 June 2003. www.futura-sciences.com

Google Earth. US Dept of State Geographer, 2015. Image Landsat.

Samiha Shafy. Iraq's Garden: Restoring the Paradise that Saddam destroyed. Spiegel Online, 3 Aug 2010. www.spiegel.de

The importance of mangroves

What is a "mangrove" forest? www.oceanservice.noaa.gov

Status and distribution of mangrove forests

of the world using earth observation satellite data. Global Ecology and Biogeography, 2010. www.dpi.inpe.br

Part 2 Water and Climate Change

Climate Change 2014: Synthesis Report. Contribution of Working Groups I, II and III to the Fifth Assessment Report of the Intergovernmental Panel on Climate Change. IPCC, 2015.

Oxfam. Entering Uncharted Water. El Nino and the threat to food security. Oxfam media briefing. 1 Oct 2015. www.oxfam.org

8 Ice and Snow Melt

National Snow & Ice Data Centre. Quick facts on ice sheets. nsidc.org

NASA Earth Observatory. Global warming and land ice. earthobservatory.nasa.gov

J Laghari. Climate change: Melting glaciers bring energy uncertainty. Nature, 30 Oct 2013. www.nature.com

United Nations Environment Programme (UNEP) and World Glacier Monitoring Service (WGMS). Global Glacier Changes: Facts and figures. 2008. www.grid.unep.ch

THINNING

World Glacier Monitoring Service. www.geo.unizh.ch

UNEP & WGMS, op cit.

North America

Climate Change 2014, op cit. p 52.

H Bernton. Snowpack drought has salmon dying in overheated rivers The Seattle Times, 25 July 2015. www.seattletimes.com

P Ford. Dead salmon, climate change and Northwest dams. The Seattle Times, 2 August 2015. www.seattletimes.com

Greenland

IPCC. Climate Change 2014: Synthesis Report. Summary. p 12. www.ipcc.ch

R Scranton. What I learned on a luxury cruise through the global-warming apocalypse. The Nation, 21 Oct 2015. www.other-news.info

The European Alps

UNEP & WGMS, op cit. 6.6 Central Europe. www.grid.unep.ch

South America

UNEP & WGMS, op cit. 6.6 South America. www.grid.unep.ch

B Francou. Global warming spells disaster for tropical Andes glaciers. The Guardian, 27 Jan 2015. www.theguardian.com

Antarctica
Antarctic ice melting so fast whole continent may be at risk by 2011. The Guardian, 12 Oct 2015. www.theguardian.com
Antarctica global warming. The effects of global warming on Antarctica. www.coolantarctica.com [accessed Oct 2015]
The Asian "water towers"
UNEP & WGMS, op cit. 6.9 Central Asia. www.grid.unep.ch
J Vidal, Most glaciers in Mount Everest area will disappear with climate change – study. The Guardian, 27 May 2015. www.theguardian.com
J Laghari, op cit.

9 Storms and Floods
Mississippi River towns rush against rising water. 18 June 2008. www.edition.cnn.com
T Logan. Why Bangladesh floods are so bad. 27 July 2004. www.bbc.co.uk
Plastic bags banned, blamed for west India floods. 29 Aug 2005. Reuters. www.planetark.com
Cost of flood damage
EM-DAT: The OFDA/CRED International Disaster Database. www.emdat.be
El Niño
NOAA Climate Prediction Center www.cpc.ncep.noaa.gov/
RISING WATERS; STORMS AND FLOODS
EM-DAT, op cit.
Mexico
Hurricane Patricia: Fears of landslides in Mexico as storm brings downpours. The Guardian, 24 Oct 2015. www.theguardian.com
China
EM-DAT, op cit.
Pakistan
Pakistan: Humanitarian Snapshot – Floods (as of 2 Oct 2014) http://reliefweb.int
Philippines
National Disaster Risk Reduction and Management Council. Republic of Philippines. Updates re the effects of typhoon "Yolanda" (Haiyan). 17 April 2014. www.ndrrmc.gov.ph
Floods in Philippines worst in 42 years. The Guardian, 27 Sept 2009. www.theguardian.com

10 Droughts
IUCN Global Drylands Initiative. www.iucn.org
24% of dryland area...
United Nations Decade for Deserts and the Fight against Desertification. www.un.org

DROUGHTS
EM-DAT: The OFDA/CRED International Disaster Database. www.emdat.be
California, USA
California's drought crisis pictures. www.cbsnews.com
Central America
Central America: Drought – 2014–15. http://reliefweb.int
Gobi Desert
R Alvarez Tudela. Fighting desertification in China. Aljazeera, 8 Dec 2012. www.aljazeera.com
Desertification affects over 18% of Chinese territory. 17 June 2006. http://english.gov.cn
Pacific Islands
Pacific: Drought – September 2015. http://reliefweb.int
East Africa
Global Weather Hazards Summary. 9 October 2015. http://reliefweb.int
Australia
O Milman. Climate change making droughts worse in Australia as rain patterns shift. The Guardian, 31 Mar 2015. www.theguardian.com
C Wahlquist. Perth's double whammy: As sea levels rise the city itself is sinking. The Guardian, 22 Oct 2015. www.theguardian.com

11 River Basin Stresses
Climate Change 2007: Working Group II: Impacts, Adaptation and Vulnerability. 3.5.1 How will climate change affect the balance of water demand and water availability? www.ipcc.ch
2016: 21 million...
SELECTED BASINS AT RISK
World Resources Institute. Aqueduct Country and River Basin Rankings. www.wri.org
Colorado River
About the Colorado River Basin. www.coloradoriverbasin.org
Reclamation press release: Colorado River basin water supply and demand study seeks input to help resolve projected future supply and demand imbalances. 29 Nov 2011. www.usbr.gov
A Maddocks, P Reig. World's 18 most stressed rivers. World Resources Institute, 20 March 2014.
Ganges–Brahmaputra
The World Delta Database. www.geol.lsu.edu/WDD/u [accessed Oct 2015].
Huang He
C Miao, J Ni, AGL Borthwick. Recent changes of water discharge and sediment load in the Yellow River basin, China. Edinburgh Research Explorer, Aug 2010.

R Guo et al. Spatial and temporal variability of annual precipitation during 1958–2007 in Loess Plateau, China. Ministry of Education Key Laboratory of Arid and Grassland Ecology, Lanzhou University.
All dried up. The Economist, 12 Oct 2013.
Dead Sea (Jordan River)
K Vick. The Dead Sea: deader than ever and getting more so. Time, 20 July 2011. www.time.com
Peter Schwartzstein. Biblical waters: can the Jordan River be saved? National Geographic, 22 Feb 2014. news.nationalgeographic.com
Zambezi
International Rivers. Zambezi, river of life. www.internationalrivers.org
International Rivers. Wrong climate for damming rivers. www.internationalrivers.org

Part 3 Water for Living

12 Water for Drinking

UNICEF WHO Joint Monitoring Report 2015. 25 years progress on sanitation and drinking water: 2015 update and MDG assessment. www.unicef.org
683 million...
WATER ACCESS
UNICEF WHO JMP 2015, op cit. p4.
DRINKING WATER
UNICEF WHO JMP data [downloaded from World Development Indicators Nov 2015].
WATER COLLECTION
UNICEF WHO JMP 2015, op cit. p31.
INEQUITY
UNICEF WHO JMP 2015, op cit. p18.

13 Water for Food

World Water Assessment Programme (WWAP). The United Nations World Water Development Report 2015: Water for a sustainable world. vol 1. UNESCO, 2015. p3, p49.
L Craymer. Beef prices sizzle with US demand. Wallstreet Journal, 10 Sept 2015. www.wsj.com/europe
UN Water. Water for Food. www.unwater.org [accessed Oct 2015]
CHANGING DIET IN CHINA
China Statistical Yearbook 2013. Beijing: China Press. 2014. www.stats.gov.cn
WATER FOR AGRICULTURE
FAO Aquastat. www.fao.org [downloaded Nov 2015].
WATER FOR FOOD
Institution of Mechanical Engineers. Global Food. Waste not want not. IME, 2013. p12. www.imeche.org

A Sedghi. How much water is needed to produce food and how much do we waste? The Guardian, 10 Jan 2013. www.theguardian.com

SOURCE OF WATER FOR AGRICULTURE
Water for Food, Water for Life. Colombo: International Water Management Institute and London: Earthscan, 2007. pp100-01.

By 2050 a 19% increase…
World Water Assessment Programme (WWAP). The United Nations World Water Development Report 4: Managing water under uncertainty and risk. UNESCO, 2012. p47.

14 Water for Sanitation
World Water Assessment Programme (WWAP). The United Nations World Water Development Report 2015: Water for a sustainable world. vol 1. UNESCO, 2015.

2.4 billion people…
UNICEF WHO Joint Monitoring Report 2015. 25 years progress on sanitation and drinking water: 2015 update and MDG assessment. www.unicef.org

90% of sewage…
S Pappas. With 7 billion people, world has a poop problem. Live Science, 25 Oct 2011. www.livescience.com

SANITATION
UNICEF WHO JMP data [downloaded from World Development Indicators Nov 2015].

WASTEWATER TREATMENT
FAO Aquastat. www.fao.org [accessed Nov 2015].

60% of India's 1.2bn people…
JMP 2015, op cit.

Constructed wetland for wastewater treatment
Wastewater solutions: artificial wetlands. 18 April 2012. www.hydratelife.org

15 Water in the City
828m urban dwellers…
INCREASING URBAN POPULATIONS
State of the World's Cities, UN-Habitat, 2010–11, p32. www.mirror.unhabitat.org

MEXICO CITY'S WATER CRISIS
Where does Mexico City get its water? Geo-Miexoc, the geography and dynamics of Modern Mexico. 9 May 2013. http://geo-mexico.com
R Jordán et al. Regional Panorama, Latin America, Megacities and Sustainability. United Nations, December 2010.
FSS Rodriguez. Exploring the risks of ineffective water supply and sewage disposal: A case study of Mexico City. Environmental Hazards 9(2), 2010. pp135–46. Taylor & Francis. www.tandfonline.com

J Watts. Failure of water supply and tanker numbers: Mexico City's water crisis – from source to sewer. The Guardian, 13 November 2015. www.theguardian.com
K Engel et al. Big Cities, Big Water, Big Challenges. Water in an urbanizing world. WWF, 2011.
Eastern Discharge Tunnel. Tunnel Emisor Oriente (TEO), Mexico City, Mexico. www.water-technology.net [accessed Nov 2015].

UNEQUAL ACCESS
Kenya National Bureau of Statistics, 2010. Mombasa Informal Settlement Survey, Kenya, 2009.
Nairobi: Kenya National Bureau of Statistics. Tables 7.1 and 7.5.

16 Water at Home
The importance of handwashing
K Greenland et al. What can hand hygiene do for the world? Environmental Health Group, Department of Disease Control, London School of Hygiene and Tropical Medicine, Oct 2012. www.hygienecentral.org.uk

WATER USE IN HOME AND LOCALITY
FAO Aquastat. www.fao.org [downloaded Nov 2015].

US RESIDENTIAL WATER USE
MA Maupin et al. Estimated use of water in the United States in 2010: US Geological Survey Circular 1405, 2014. http://pubs.usgs.gov

DECLINING USE
ibid. pp19-21.

WATER IN THE HOME
Water – The facts. Waterwise, 2012. www.waterwise.org

THE TRUE COST OF WATER
Make the drops to watts connection. EPA, August 2014. www3.epa.gov

17 Water and Disease
MC Freeman MC et al. Hygiene and health: systematic review of handwashing practices worldwide and update of health effects. Trop Med Int Health. 19(8), 2014. pp906–16. www.ncbi.nlm.nih.gov
A Prüss-Üstün et al. Burden of disease from inadequate water, sanitation and hygiene in low- and middle-income settings: a retrospective analysis of data from 145 countries. Tropical Medicine & International Health. 19 (8), 2014. pp894–905. www.ncbi.nlm.nih.gov

Trachoma
Trachoma. WHO Fact Sheet 382. May 2015. www.who.int

DEATHS FROM DIARRHOEA
Prüss-Üstün et al, op cit, 2014.

MALARIA
Achieving the Malaria MDG Target. Reversing the incidence of malaria 2000–2015. Unicef and World Health Organization, 2014. Annex 1A, p29. www.who.int

40% of the world's population Between 2000 and 2013…
www.who.int

BLIGHTED LIVES
Onchocerciasis. WHO Fact sheet 374. Mar 2015.
Schistosomiasis.
10 facts about Schistosomiasis.
Neglected tropical diseases. www.who.int

Part 4 Water for Economic Production

18 Water Footprint
CONTRASTING WATER FOOTPRINTS
EMBEDDED WATER
MM Mekonnen, AY Hoekstra. National water footprint accounts: the green, blue and grey water footprint of production and consumption. Value of Water Research Report Series No. 50. UNESCO-IHE, Delft, the Netherlands, 2011. Appendix X.

GLOBAL FOOTPRINTS
22% of water consumed
Mekonnen and Hoekstra, op cit. vol 1, Fig 13, p32.

19 Water for Irrigation
World Water Assessment Programme (WWAP). The United Nations World Water Development Report: Water for people, water for life. UNESCO and Berghahn Book. 2003. Chap 8.
Water for Food, Water for Life: A comprehensive assessment of water management in agriculture. Colombo: International Water Management Institute and London: Earthscan, 2007. www.iwmi.cgiar.org
A Hamdy. Water demand management in the Mediterranean. Paper prepared for 2nd Regional Workshop on Water Resource Management, held on 2–4 April 2000, at the Eastern Mediterranean University (EMU) in northern Cyprus. www.idrc.ca

WATER WITHDRAWALS FOR IRRIGATION
MA Maupin et al. Estimated use of water in the United States in 2010. US Geological Survey Circular 1405, 2014.

IRRIGATED LAND
FAO Aquastat. www.fao.org [downloaded Nov 2015].

Deficit irrigation
World Water Assessment Programme (WWAP). The United Nations World Water Development Report 2015: Water for a sustainable world. vol 1. UNESCO, 2015. p49.

20 Water for Fisheries
FAO. The State of World Fisheries and Aquaculture. Infographics. www.fao.org
Vital signs, Worldwatch Institute. http://vitalsigns.worldwatch.org/
Fish to 2030. Prospects for Fisheries and Aquaculture. World Bank report 83177-GLB. The World Bank, 2013. www.fao.org
Fish farms to produce nearly two thirds of global food fish supply by 2030, report shows. The World Bank, press release. 5 Feb 2014. [tons converted to tonnes] www.worldbank.org
Trafficked into slavery on Thai trawlers to catch food for prawns. The Guardian, 11 June 2014. www.theguardian.com

FISH CONSUMED
RATE OF CHANGE
The State of World Fisheries and Aquaculture: Opportunities and challenges. FAO. 2014. Table 11, p29.

Threat to local economy
China illegally fishing off coast of West Africa, Greenpeace study reveals. Agence France-Presse, reported in The Guardian, 20 May 2015.
C Kende-Robb. Why illegal fishing off Africa's coast must be stopped. The Guardian, 19 June 2014.

AQUACULTURE
Table A-0(a) World fisheries production, by capture and aquaculture, by country (2013). FAO. ftp://ftp.fao.org

INCREASE IN AQUACULTURE
Table A-4 World aquaculture production of fish, crustaceans, molluscs, etc., by principal producers in 2013. FAO.

Fish farming
State of World Fisheries and Aquaculture 2014. FAO. Table 10, p28. www.fao.org

21 Water for Industry
Global water demand...
World Water Assessment Programme (WWAP). The United Nations World Water Development Report 2015: Water for a sustainable world. UNESCO, 2015 p 58.

WATER FOR FUEL
Data from Sandia National Laboratories, US Department of Energy and Energy Information Administration. Cited on http://biofuel.org.uk/water.html

INDUSTRIAL WATER USE
FAO Aquastat. www.fao.org [accessed Nov 2015].

MAKING WATER WORK
WWAP Facts and Figures, citing Margat and Andréassian, 2008. www.unesco.org

Chile
Esperanza. http://english.mineraesperanza.cl

22 Water for Energy
World Commission on Dams. Dams and development. A new framework for decision making. Earthscan, 2000. p14. www.internationalrivers.org
United Nations Industrial Development Organization (UNIDO). Water and energy. In: World Water Assessment Programme (WWAP): The United Nations World Water Development Report 2: Water – A shared responsibility. UNESCO and Berghahn Books. 2006. p322.
World Water Assessment Programme facts www.unesco.org
Ethiopia's biggest dam oversized, experts say. International Rivers. 5 Sept 2013. www.internationalrivers.org

An increase in electricity...
World Water Assessment Programme (WWAP). The United Nations World Water Development Report 2015: Water for a sustainable world. UNESCO, 2015. p54.

GLOBAL ELECTRICITY GENERATION
Key World Energy Statistics 2015. OECD/IEA, 2015. p24.

THERMO-ELECTRIC POWER
MA Maupin et al. Estimated use of water in the United States in 2010: U.S. Geological Survey Circular 1405. USCS, 2014. Table 12. http://pubs.usgs.gov

HYDROPOWER
World Development Indicators. World Bank. [downloaded Nov 2015].
Key World Energy Statistics 2015. OECD/IEA, 2015, p19

HYDROPOWER IN CHINA
True cost of hydropower in China. International Rivers Network. 23 Nov 2014. www.internationalrivers.org

GROWTH OF HYDROPOWER
Key World Energy Statistics 2015. OECD/IEA, 2015. p18.

23 Transport and Leisure
G Flaccus. Here's how California golf courses are responding to the historic drought. Associated Press. 13 May 2015. www.techinsider.io

Golf courses in the USA...
K Gammon. In face of drought, golf tries to reduce water use. Science News Service, 18 June 2015. www.insidescience.org as [2.08bn gallons = 7.87bn litre].

WATERBOURNE FREIGHT IN USA
Waterborne Commerce of the United States. Calendar Year 2012. Part 5 – National Summaries. Institute for Water Resources, Navigation Data Center. US Army Corps of Engineers. Table 2-1. www.navigationdatacenter.us

Great Lakes
ibid. Table 3-10.

Mississippi
ibid. Table 3-5.

China's waterways
China Statistical Yearbook 2014. Beijing: China Press, 2015. Tables 18-3 and 18-8. www.stats.gov.cn

Golf courses
Gammon, op cit.
Flaccus, op cit.

24 Water for Sale
World Water Assessment Programme (WWAP): The United Nations World Water Development Report 2: Water – A shared responsibility. UNESCO and Berghahn Books. 2006.

In developing countries...
WWAP Facts and Figures. Charging for Water? www.unesco.org

PRICE OF PIPED WATER
Managing Water for All: An OECD perspective on pricing and financing. OECD, 2009. pp87–88. Cited in WWDR2, chap 12, fig 12.5.

RELATIVE COST OF WATER
Water and Sanitation in the World's Cities. UN-Habitat, Nairobi. Earthscan, 2003.

BOTTLED WATER
Bottled Water Reporter. International Bottled Water Association, Jul/Aug 2015. www.bottledwater.org
O Balch. The madness of drinking bottled water shipped halfway round the world. The Guardian, 9 July 2015. www.theguardian.com
S Cardoni. The United States of Bottled Water: Our thirst for liquid fool's gold. Take Part, 4 Sept 2011. www.takepart.com
Bottled water bans. www.google.com/maps/

Estimated energy to produce, package...
PH Gleick and HS Cooley. Energy implications of bottled water. Environmental Research Letters, 2009. Downloaded from http://iopscience.iop.org/

US annual consumption…
TOP TEN MARKETS
Bottled Water Reporter. International
  Bottled Water Association, Jul/Aug
  2015. http://issuu.com/ibwa/docs/bwr_
  julyaug2015_final
WATER IN BOTTLES OR SACHETS
World Water Assessment Programme
  (WWAP). The United Nations World
  Water Development Report 2015: Water
  for a sustainable world. UNESCO, 2015.
  p39.

Part 5 Damaged Water

25 Dammed Rivers
Commission Internationale des Grand
  Barrages / International Commission on
  Large Dams. Register of dams.
  www.icold-cigb.org [accessed Nov
  2015].
66% of the world's large river systems
Global Biodiversity Outlook 3. Secretariat
  of the Convention on Biological
  Diversity, 2010. p43.
Greenhouse gas emissions
4% of global warming due to dams, says
  new research. 9 May 2007.
  www.internationalrivers.org
Frequently asked questions: Greenhouse
  gas emissions from dams. May 2007.
  www.internationalrivers.org
**ENVIRONMENTAL STRESS DUE TO
FLOW ALTERATION**
Map supplied by Center for Environmental
  Systems Research, University of Kassel,
  Nov 2014, Water GAP3.
Mississippi Delta
C Nilsson, C Reidy. Dams in the world. In:
  Dams under debate. Formas, 2006. p6.
  www.formas.se
Colorado River
Colorado River. Setting the Course.
  www.coloradoriverbasin.org
Hyrdopower in Patagonia
B Clark Howard. Chile scraps huge
  Patagonia dam project after years of
  controversy. National Geographic, 10
  June 2014.
  www.news.nationalgeographic.com
China
Hydropower projects on the Salween
  river: an update. Salween Watch, 14 Mar
  2014. www.internationalrivers.org
Indian dams
India. www.internationalrivers.org
K Cooke. India's dam-building bonanza.
  16 Mar 2014.
  www.climatenewsnetwork.net
Murray–Darling, Australia
Restoring the balance of the Murray–
  Darling basin. Department of the
  Environment, Water, Heritage and the
  Arts, Australia. May 2010.
  www.environment.gov.au
African Water Power
RA Sanyanga. Right priorities for Africa's
  power sector. 20 Oct 2015.
  www.internationalrivers.org
WORLD DAMS
Commission Internationale des Grands
  Barrages/International Commission on
  Large Dams. General synthesis. Number
  of dams by country members.
  www.icold-cigb.org
  [accessed Nov 2015].

26 Dispossession by Water
Up to 80 million people…
Human impacts of dams. International
  Rivers Network, citing the World
  Commission on Dams.
  www.internationalrivers.org
Dams and Disease
M McCartney et al. Large dams and
  malaria in Sub-Saharan Africa . 11 Sept
  2015. https://wle.cgiar.org
Damming statistics.
  www.internationalrivers.org
THE DAMNED
Source for information on specific dams,
  unless otherwise stated: International
  Rivers www.internationalrivers.org
Bargi, Madhya Pradesh, India 1990
New Internationalist, July 2001.
  www.netint.org
Chixoy, Guatemala
BR Johnston. Chixoy Dam Legacy Issues
  Study. Centre for Political Ecology, Santa
  Cruz, California, Mar 2005.
  www.internationalrivers.org
Lesotho Highlands, Lesotho
K Horta, L Pottinger. A big idea for aiding
  Africa – think small. Los Angeles Times,
  21 Sept 2005.
Manantali, Senegal
World Commission on Dams. Dams and
  Development. A new framework for
  decision making. Earthscan, 2000. p14.
  www.internationalrivers.org
Sobradinho, Bahia, Brazil
Movements occupy the hydroelectric plant
  of Sobradinho in the state of Barragens.
  10 June 2008. www.mabnacional.org.br
Three Gorges, Yangtze
J Yardley. Chinese dam projects criticized
  for their human cost. New York Times, 19
  Nov 2007.
Tipaimukh, Manipur, India
J Yumnam. Damned hearings of proposed
  Tipaimukh Dam. www.kanglaonline.com
Yacyretá, Argentina-Paraguay
Final report of the Panel of the
  Independent Investigation Mechanism on
  Yacyretá Hydroelectric Project, 27 Feb
  2004. www.internationalrivers.com

27 Water Pollutants
E Corcoran et al. (eds). Sick Water? The
  central role of wastewater management
  in sustainable development. A rapid
  response assessment. United Nations
  Environment Programme, UN-HABITAT,
  GRID-Arendal, 2010. www.unep.org
World Water Assessment Programme Facts
  and Figures: www.unesco.org
Water: a matter of life and death.
  www.un.org/events
Persistent organic pollutants. A global
  issue, a global response. www.epa.gov
Around 50% of phosphorus…
Rockström et al, 2009a, cited in E
  Corcoran, op cit. p.31.
**ORGANIC AND NON-ORGANIC
POLLUTANTS**
World Water Assessment Programme
  (WWAP). The United Nations World
  Water Development Report 2: Water –
  a shared responsibility. UNESCO and
  Berghahn Books, 2006. Table 4.5. p141.
ORGANIC POLLUTION
World Bank, 2011, World Development
  Indicators, pp146–49, cited by WWAP
  Indicators – Industry and Energy
  www.unesco.org
NITROGEN IN WASTEWATER
Nitrogen effluents are…
X Leflaive et al. OECD Environmental
  Outlook to 2050: The consequences of
  inaction. OECD Publishing, 2012.
  Chap 5.

28 Water Pollution
E Corcoran et al. (eds). Sick Water? The
  central role of wastewater management
  in sustainable development. A rapid
  response assessment. United Nations
  Environment Programme, UN-HABITAT,
  GRID-Arendal, 2010. www.unep.org
World Water Assessment Programme
  (WWAP). The United Nations World
  Water Development Report 2: Water –
  a shared responsibility. UNESCO and
  Berghahn Books, 2006. Chaps 4 and 8.
There are over 400…
B Palmer. Devil in the deep blue sea.
  www.onearth.org [accessed Jan 2016].
San Joaquin river
America's most endangered rivers for
  2014: San Joaquin. American Rivers.
  americanrivers.org [accessed Jan 2016].
T Stokely: Ending selenium pollution of
  the San Joaquin River and Bay-Delta.
  California Water Impact Network, 19
  May 2010. www.c-win.org

California's San Joaquin River is nation's most endangered in 2014, conservation group says. Circle of Blue, 9 April 2014. www.circleofblue.org

Gulf of Mexico
2015 Gulf of Mexico dead zone "above average". 4 June 2015. http://noaanew.noaa.gov

Baltic Sea
LM Svendsen et al. Inputs of nitrogen and phosphorus to the Baltic Sea. HELCOM core indicator report, 2015. www.helcom.fi [accessed 4 Jan 2016].

China
Pollution status on: www.chinawaterrisk.org [accessed Jan 2015].
Nine biggest water pollution disasters in China (since 2010). 15 April 2014. www.globaltimes.cn

Bangladesh
SV Flanagan, RB Johnston, Y Zheng. Arsenic in tube well water in Bangladesh: health and economic impacts and implications for arsenic mitigation. Bulletin of the World Health Organization. vol 90, 2012. pp839-846. www.who.int
S Gilbert. Arsenic poisoning in Bangladesh. 30 May 2014. www.toxipedia.org

India
M McDermott. Eighty percent of India's sewage goes untreated into city water supplies. 7 Mar 2013. http://motherboard.vice.com
M McDermott. River Ganga still holy, but it's also causing record levels of cancer in people living nearby. 17 Oct 2012. www.treehugger.com

Tigris and Euphrates
MN Shamout, G Lahn. The Euphrates in Crisis: Channels of cooperation for a threatened river. Chatham House. The Royal Institute of International Affairs. April 2015. www.chathamhouse.org

29 Damaged Waterways

World Water Assessment Programme (WWAP). The United Nations World Water Development Report 2: Water – a shared responsibility. UNESCO and Berghahn Books, 2006. Chaps 4 and 8.

Contaminated drinking water, Flint, USA
R Felton. Michigan city to change water source after studies showed lead increase. The Guardian, 8 Oct 2015. www.theguardian.com
J Walters. Flint's "toxic soup" polluted water worse for children than thought, doctor says. The Guardian, 17 Dec 2015.
T Laylin. How Michigan's Flint River is poisoning the city's residents. The Guardian, 18 Jan 2016.

Samarco Mine, Brazil
H Araujo. Brazil toxic mudslide devastates local water supply. The Guardian, 19 Nov 2015.
Brazil dam toxic mud reaches Atlantic via Rio Doce estuary. BBC News, 22 Nov 2015. www.bbc.co.uk
Reuters. Mud from Brazil dam disaster is toxic, UN says, despite mine operator denials. The Guardian, 26 Nov 2015. www.theguardian.com

Baia Mare tailings dams, Romania
WWWR2, op cit. p283.
M Bacsujlaky. Examples of modern mines that damaged rivers & fishers. 2004 Oct. www.bristolbayalliance.com

Aniline leak, China
Nine biggest water pollution disasters in China (since 2010). Global Times, 15 April 2014. globaltimes.cn

Environmental activism, China
K McDonald. Chinese enviro group uses hazmat suits to protect a river. 23 Dec 2015. www.pacificenvironment.org

Earthquake, Turkey
WWWR2, op cit. p.281

Yamuna River, India
R Kaur. The most polluted river Yamuna. www.mapsofindia.com

30 Threatened Ecologies

CM Finlayson, et al. Ecosystems and Human Well-being: Wetlands and water. Millennium Ecosystem Assessment. World Resources Institute, 2005. Chap 20.
Freshwater Ecosystems of the World – WWF/TNC. 2008. www.feow.org
IUCN. Overview of the IUCN Red List. www.iucnredlist.org
United States Environmental Protection Agency (EPA). Why are wetlands important? www.epa.gov
ZSL. The SampleD Red List index. www.zsl.org

MOLLUSCS
Finlayson, op cit. p.563.

RELATIVE SPECIES RICHNESS
ibid. p.26.

ENDANGERED SPECIES

Waterbirds and wetland-dependent birds
BirdLife International 2008. Cited on: Waterbirds are showing widespread declines. www.birdlife.org

Wetland-dependent mammals

Freshwater amphibians

Freshwater fish
Caring for Wetlands: An answer to climate change. Ramsar Convention on Wetlands, 2010. p4. www.ramsar.org

Freshwater turtles

Crocodiles
IUCN Redlist, Table 4a. www.iucnredlist.org

Freshwater crayfish and crabs
IUCN Summary Statistics. Figure 3. www.iucnredlist.org

Part 6 Water for the Future

31 Technological Fixes

W Henley. The new water technologies that could save the planet. The Guardian, 22 July 2013. www.theguardian.com
PH Gleick et al. With a grain of salt. In: The World's Water 2006/07. Island Press, 2006. pp51–89.
Tapping the oceans. The Economist, 5 June 2008. www.economist.com

Innovative check-dams
India Water Portal flikr photo collection. Shree Patel collection: Sisandra, Madaka, Kerala.

DESALINATION
FAO Aquastat. www.fao.org [downloaded Jan 2015].

USA

Spain
Tapping the oceans. op. cit.

London
How the treatment works operates. www.thameswater.co.uk

Tackling excessive fluoride
M Black, R Talbot. Water: A matter of life and health. UNICEF and OUP India, 2005. pp202–06.
J Fawell et al. Fluoride in Drinking Water. WHO-IWA, 2006.

Intelligent irrigation
P Hitchin. Seawater greenhouses: growing food in the world's driest regions. Engineering and Technology Magazine. vol 9(6), 16 June 2014. http://eandt.theiet.org/index.cfm
Seawater Greenhouse www.seawatergreenhouse.com

32 The Rising Price of Water

J Kjellsson, S Liu. International Water Pricing. 27 March 2012. www.caee.utexas.edu

AS SUPPLIES DIMINISH, COSTS INCREASE
Where does Mexico City get its water? 9 May 2013. http://geo-mexico.com/
ND Ruilstia. Coastal area needs absorption wells. The Jakarta Post, 8 Oct 2011. www.thejakartapost.com/

COST OF WATER EXTRACTION FOR IRRIGATION
United States Department of Agriculture (USDA) Economic Research Service. Western Irrigated Agriculture, Tables 4-2b, 4-5b, 4-6b. www.ers.usda.gov

Right2Water: Ireland erupts
M Piggott. Ireland: 80,000 march in protest at austerity linked new water charges. International Business Times, 30 August 2015. www.ibtimes.co.uk
Tens of thousands march through Dublin to protest against water charges. The Guardian, 21 March 2015. www.theguardian.com

Tanzania
UK water company fails in $20 million compensation claim from Tanzanian government. World Development Movement, 28 July 2008. www.wdm.org.uk

Manila, Philippines
J Jowit. Experts call for hike in global water price. The Guardian, 27 April 2010. www.theguardian.com
J Vidal. Water privatisation: a worldwide failure? The Guardian, 30 January 2015. www.theguardian.com

Bolivia
New Internationalist. 338. Sept 2001. www.newint.org

Guyana
UK wastes millions of pounds of aid on failed water privatisation in Guyana. World Development Movement. 19 Feb 2007. www.waterjustice.org

33 Treaties and Obligations
A human right
The human right to water and sanitation. Milestones. www.un.org
Status of the Watercourses Convention. International Water Law project. www.internationalwaterlaw.org [accessed Jan 2016].
WATER TREATIES
BASIN TREATIES
Transboundary Freshwater Dispute Database. Department of Geosciences, Oregon State University, 2008. www.transboundarywaters.orst.edu

34 Striving for Co-operation
UN Water Organisation fact sheet: Transboundary Water. www.unwater.org
WATER ISSUES
CONFLICT AND CO-OPERATION
Transboundary Freshwater Dispute Database, Oregon State University, 2008. www.transboundarywaters.orst.edu
THE NEED FOR CO-OPERATION
The Colorado
Colorado River Boundary Section. International Boundary & Water Commission. United States and Mexico. www.ibwc.state.gov

Colorado River: Mexico and US sign water-sharing deal. 21 Nov 2012. BBC News. www.bbc.co.uk
T Gaynor. US–Mexico water pact brings life back to Colorado River's parched delta. 27 April 2015. Aljazeera America. www.america.aljazeera.com
The Danube
International Commission for the Protection of the Danube River. www.icpdr.org
Tigris–Euphrates basin
Z Sabah, et al. Water shortages unite Iraq, Islamic State against Turkey. Bloomberg Business. 1 July 2015. www.bloomberg.com
The Indus
MA Notezai. Interview: The India–Pakistan water dispute. The Diplomat, 21 Nov 2014. http://thediplomat.com
The Mekong
Mekong River Commission www.mrcmekong.org
Dam Projects ignite a legal battle over Mekong River's future. National Geographic, 11 July 2014. http://news.nationalgeographic.com/
Lake Chad
EO Odada. Lake Chad. Experience and lessons learned brief. 7 Feb 2006. www.ilec.or.jp
The Nile
Nile Basin Initiative. www.nilebasin.org
S Mwangi et al. The limits of the new "Nile Agreement". 28 April 2015. www.brookings.edu

35 Managing the Future
Open Working Group proposal for Sustainable Development Goals. https://sustainabledevelopment.un.org
Charting Our Water Future, 2030 Water Resources Group, 2009. www.mckinsey.com
40% of respondents…
Global risks perception survey, 2015. World Economic Forum. Cited in Water Footprint Network newsletter, January 2015.
www.waterfootprint.org
Armenia: local solutions for wastewater management
Local solutions for waste water management in Armenia village. Case study no. 438. www.gwp.org
Cameroon: protecting Lake Ossa
Local initiative to protect Lake Ossa. Case study no. 363. www.gwp.org

SURVEY OF INTEGRATED WATER RESOURCES MANAGEMENT
UNEP 2012. The UN-Water Status Report on the Application of Integrated Approaches to Water Resources Management. Figure 1.3. Questionnaire submission status. p7.
SURVEY RESPONSE: STATUS OF MAIN PLANS
ibid. Fig 2.3 Integrated Water Resources Management Plan(s) or Equivalent. p13.
PROGRESS ON IWRM PLANNING
ibid. Fig 2.5 Progress from 2008 to 2012 on Implementation of National/Federal Water Laws by HDI Groups
Women and water management
WaterAid. www.wateraid.org

Part 7 Tables and Sources
Needs and Resources
Col 1: UN Population Division. World population prospects: the 2015 revision.
Col 2: UN Population Division. World urbanization prospects: the 2014 revision.
Cols 3 & 4: UNICEF and WHO Joint Monitoring Programme.
Cols 5 – 9: FAO Aquastat [downloaded Oct 2015–Feb 2016].
Water Uses
Cols 1, 2 & 4: FAO Aquastat. [Downloaded Feb 2016].
Col 3: www.waterfootprint.org [downloaded Nov 2015].
Col 5: World Development Indicators online. [downloaded Nov 2015].
Col 6: FAO. World fisheries production, by capture and aquaculture, by country (2013)
Col 7: www.ramsar.org [downloaded Nov 2015].

INDEX

Africa
    access to water 46
    agricultural water use 48, 49
    bottled water 73
    collection of water 46
    cost of water 72
    dams 68, 77, 79
    disease 56, 57
    drought 41
    fisheries 64
    pollution 81
    shared river basins 96
    urban population increase 52
    water scarcity 23
agriculture *see also* irrigation
    pollution by 80–81, 82–83, 84–85
    water used by 26–27, 48–49, 60, 61
algal blooms 82, 83, 86
Amazon basin
    dams 78
    tourism 70
Angola, price of water 72
Antarctic 35, 36
Argentina
    dams 78
    pollution 81
    wastewater treatment 51
Armenia, wastewater management 98
aquaculture 59, 64–65
    impact of 32, 59, 64
aquifers 28
    exhaustion of 12, 19, 28, 40, 41, 73
    "fossil water" 19, 28
    pollution of 82, 83
    recharge of 20, 28
    salination of 28
aridity zones 22–23
arsenic contamination 83
Australia
    dams 77
    drought 41
    industrialized farming 23
    Perth 23, 41
    pollution 81
    price of water 72
    water shortage 23

Baltic Sea, algal bloom 83
Bangladesh
    arsenic contamination 83
    flooding 38
biofuels 66
Bolivia
    dispute with Chile 30
    privatization of water supply 93
bottled water 59, 73
Brazil
    bottled water 73
    dams 78, 84
    hydropower 69
    pollution 84
    water resources 22

Cambodia, Tonle Sap 33
California, USA
    Arcata wetlands wastewater treatment 50
    deficit irrigation 63
    drought 40, 71
    floods 40
    golf courses 70, 71
    San Joaquin river basin 28, 63, 82
Cameroon 98
Canada 36; *see also* North America
    dams 77
    hydropower 69
    price of water 72
canals 70, 71
Caribbean
    fisheries 64
    poor water infrastructure 52
    urban population increase 52
Central America
    drought 35, 40
    sewerage 50
    storms 38
Central Asia
    agricultural water use 49
    competition for water 30, 31
    pollution 81
Chad, Lake 97
check-dams 28, 62, 90
Chile
    dam proposal 76
    dispute with Bolivia 30
    seawater pipeline 66
China
    aquaculture 64
    bottled water 73
    changing diet 48
    citizens pressure groups 83, 85
    contamination *see* pollution
    dams 68, 77, 78, 79, 97
    deficit irrigation 62, 63
    desertification 41
    floods 39
    groundwater stress 29
    hydropower 69
    pollution 81, 83, 85
    population 22
    rivers 24, 33, 39, 43, 60, 79, 97
    wastewater treatment 51
    waterborne freight 70, 71
    water resources 22, 25
    wetlands 33
cities *see* urban dwellers
climate change 19, 20, 24, 32, 35–43, 68, 77
coastal ecosystems 80, 82, 83
Colorado river basin 24, 42, 76, 95, 96
Columbia River 36
Convention on Wetlands, Ramsar 32–33

dams 28, 31
    environmental impact of 32, 38, 40, 76–77
    for irrigation water 62
    impact on humans of 76, 77, 78–79
    hydropower 68, 76, 77
    potential for conflict 30, 31, 97
Danube river basin 84, 95, 97
deforestation 38
dengue 57
desalination 89, 90–91
desertification 40, 41
diseases related to water 54, 56–57
domestic water use 26–27, 54, 55, 59
drinking water *see* water supply
droughts 24, 35, 40–41, 42, 43
drylands 22–23, 40–41

Egypt, water conflict 97
El Niño 35, 38, 40, 41
electricity *see* energy; thermo-electric power; hydropower
embedded water 19, 26, 60–61
endemic species 86
energy
    demand for 26
    water used to produce 26, 68–69
Ethiopia, Grand Ethiopian Renaissance Dam 68, 97
Europe
    Alps 37
    bottled water 73
    dams 77
    fisheries 64
    pollution 81
    waterways 70, 71
excreta, human 14, 50, 75, 80

fertilizers, pollution by 75, 80, 82, 85
fish 64–65
    threat to 64, 76
    farming of *see* aquaculture
floods 35, 38–39, 42, 43
    protection from 33
fluoride filters 91
food *see also* fish
    changing diets 45, 48
    pollution by production of 80, 81
    water used to produce 13, 26–27, 45, 48–49, 60, 62
France
    bottled water 73
    dams 77
    hydropower 69
    pollution 81
    price of water 72
freshwater ecosystems 35, 86–87
    damage to 75, 76, 80, 86

Ganges–Brahmaputra basin 43, 83, 95
Germany
    bottled water 73

dams 77
   price of water 72
Ghana
   bottled water 73
   dams 78
   pollution 81
   wastewater treatment 51
glaciers 20, 21
   melting of 36–37
global warming *see* climate change
golf courses 70, 71
Great Lakes 70
Greenland 35, 37
greenhouse gases 43, 68, 76
groundwater 24, 28–29; *see also* aquifers
Guatemala, dams 78
Guyana, privatization of water supply 93

handwashing 54, 56
heavy metals 80, 81, 84
Himalayas 25, 36, 37
Huang He basin 24, 43
hydrological cycle 19, 20–21, 36
hydropower 68, 69, 76, 77, 78, 79
   small hydropower 68

ice 20, 21
   melting 35, 36–37, 38
India
   competition for water 31, 97
   dams 77, 78, 79
   groundwater 29
   hydropower 69
   Mumbai 38
   pollution 81
   population 22
   rivers 31, 43, 83, 95, 97
   sewage contamination 83, 85
   tourism 71
   water footprint 60
   wastewater treatment 51, 83, 85
   water resources 22, 25, 29
Indonesia
   aquifer salination 92
   bottled water 73
   pollution 81
   price of water 72
Indus River 37, 97
Indus Waters Treaty 96, 97
industry
   pollution by 80–81, 82–83, 84–85
   water used by 26–27, 59, 60, 61,
     66–67
Integrated Water Resources Management
   98, 99
International Panel on Climate Change 35
invasive species 86
Iran
   dams 77
   pollution 81
   water stress 29
Iraq
   ISIL, control of water 31
   soil salinity 23
   southern marshlands 33

Ireland, Republic of, protests 93
irrigation 12, 13, 26, 48, 49, 62–63, 92
   cause of soil salinity 23, 62
   dams for 62
   deficit 62, 63
   intelligent 91
   use of groundwater 49, 62
   water resources for 42
Israel, Jordan River 43
Italy
   dams 77
   price of water 72

Japan
   dams 77
   hydropower 69
   pollution 81
   price of water 72
Jordan River 43

Kenya
   Mombasa water and sewage 53
   price of water 72
Kazakhstan, inequity in water access 47
Korea, South
   dams 77
   pollution 81
   price of water 72

Laos, dam 79
Latin America
   agricultural water use 49
   fisheries 64
   pollution 81
   urban population increase 52
Lesotho, dam 79
Libya, water shortage 29

malaria 57
   mosquito breeding sites 78
Mali, Niger Inner Delta 33
mangroves 32; *see also* wetlands
Mekong River 33, 97
   Commission 97
Mexico
   bottled water consumption 73
   City water supply 28, 53, 92
   dams 77
   Gulf of, algal bloom 82
   price of water 72
   storms and floods 38
Middle East
   agricultural water use 49
   ISIL 31
   Jordan River 43
Millennium Development Goals 52
mining, pollution by 75, 82, 83
Mississippi river basin 38, 70, 76, 82
municipal water use 26–27
Murray–Darling river basin 24, 77

New Zealand,
   pollution 81
Nile 71, 95
   Basin Initiative 30, 97

competition for waters of 30, 94, 96, 97
   dams on 68, 97
nitrogen 80, 81
North America
   climate change 36
   fisheries 64
   pollution 81
   water use 22
Norway
   dams 77
   hydropower 69
   price of water 72

Oceania, fisheries 64
onchocerciasis 57

Pacific islands, drought 41
Pakistan
   competition for water 97
   deficit irrigation 62
   floods 39
   groundwater stress 29
   pollution 81
   water resources 25
Paraguay, dams 78
persistent organic pollutants (POPs) 75, 80
Peru, price of water 72
pesticides 42, 75, 80, 82, 84
Philippines
   pollution 81
   privatization of water supply 93
   storms and floods 39
phosphorus 80
pollution 80–81, 82–83, 84–85
population
   density 22
   growth 22, 25, 30, 40
   in water-stressed areas 22, 24
   urban 52

rainfall 20
   variability 20, 24, 25, 35, 36, 38, 42, 43
rainwater harvesting 28, 90
reservoirs 24, 26, 31, 40, 53, 70, 78, 79,
   83, 85
   disease-vector breeding in 78
   emissions from 43, 68, 76
   evaporation from 42, 43, 68
   sediment in 38, 76
Rio Grande 24, 95
river basins 42–43
   overstretched 42–43
   treaties 94–95, 96–97
rivers 20
   contamination of 75, 82–83, 84–85
   flow variability 19, 42, 43, 69, 77
   fragmentation of 75, 76–77
   transport on 70–71
Romania, pollution 85
rural dwellers
   access to water 46, 47, 50,
   coping with water shortage 28
   small hydropower 68

Russia
  hydropower 69
  pollution 81

Sahara 29, 40
salt water 20, 21
  intrusion in freshwater aquifers 28, 92
sanitation, access to 50–51
schistosomiasis 57, 78
sea-level rise 20, 36
sediment 32, 42, 76, 80, 84
Senegal, dam 79
sewage
  contamination by 83, 85
  leakage of 52, 82
  systems 50, 52, 53, 85
snowfall, variability 36, 37
storms 38–39
soil 19, 32, 40, 75, 76
  contamination of 66, 85
  erosion of 38, 39
  fertility 20
  moisture 45, 48, 59, 60
  salinity 23, 62
South Africa
  dams 77
  pollution 81
  price of water 72
  wastewater treatment 51
  water law 94
Spain
  dams 77
  desalination 91
  price of water 72
Sudan 30,
  Nile Waters Agreement 96, 97
  dams 79
Sustainable Development Goals 98
Sweden, price of water 72
Syria
  dependence 97
  refugees from 43

Tanzania
  pollution 81
  privatization of water supply 93
technological fixes 90–91
temperature increase
  air 35, 36, 40, 42
  water 35, 42
Thailand
  dam 79
  pollution 81
  wastewater treatment 51
thermo-electric power stations 68
Three Gorges dam 79
Tigris–Euphrates basin
  damming of rivers 31, 83, 96, 97
  pollution of 83
toilets 53, 83, 85
tourism 70–71
  impact on mangroves 32
trachoma 56

Turkey
  bottled water 73
  dams 77, 79
  pollution 81, 85
Uganda
  price of water 72
  Nile Basin 30
  pollution 81
UK
  bottled water 73
  canals 70
  dams 77
  desalination 91
  pollution 81
  price of water 72
  privatization 93
  wastewater treatment 51
  water footprint 60
United Nations
  Convention on the Law of Non-
    Navigational Uses of International
    Watercourses (2014) 94, 96
  Human Rights Council resolution 94
  recognition of right to water and
    sanitation 94
urban dwellers
  access to improved water source 47, 53
  access to improved sanitation 52, 53
  number of 52
  slum dwellers 52
urbanization 22
  dependence on groundwater 28
  flooding 38
  pollution of water 42
USA see also North America; California;
  Colorado River
  agriculture 48, 92
  aquifers 28–29
  bottled water 73
  dams 77
  desalination 90
  El Niño effects 38, 40
  Florida Everglades 32
  golf courses 70, 71
  irrigation 62, 63, 92
  Las Vegas 22
  meat consumption 48
  pollution 81, 82, 84
  price of water 72
  residential water use 54, 55
  rivers 24, 38, 42
  thermo-electric power 68
  treaty with Mexico 96
  wastewater treatment 51
  waterborne freight 70
  water footprint 60
  water shortage 24
  wetlands 32, 50

Vietnam
  dams 79
virtual water 60–61

wastewater 50, 75, 81
  cost of disposal 72
  recycling of 90
  treatment of 50, 51, 53, 60, 80, 85, 98
water see also drinking water
  "blue" 49, 60, 62
  competition for 12, 19, 25, 30–31
  conflict over 30–31, 96–97
  conservation 13, 53
  contamination of see pollution of
  co-operation over 14, 15, 89, 94–97
  cycle 20–21
  demand for 11, 12, 19, 24, 25, 26–27,
    89
  dependency 30–31
  disease transmission 56, 57
  distribution of 19, 22–23
  diversion of 30
  economic productivity of 59–73
  embedded 12, 19, 26, 60
  footprint 14, 60–61
  "green" 49, 60, 62
  impoundment of 76–77, 78–79
  inefficient use of 60
  management of 15, 19, 30, 35, 75
  pollution of 14, 32, 42, 60, 75, 80–81,
    82–83, 84–85
  price of 12, 92, 93
  purification 90–91
  renewable supply of 21
  shortages 24–25
  treaties governing use 94–95
  transport on 70–71
  vapour 20
  virtual 61, 62
  withdrawals of 25, 26–27, 28, 29, 62
water supply 46–47, 72–73
  access to 12, 45, 46–47
  bottled 73
  collection of 45, 46
  contamination of 75, 82, 84, 85
  cost of 72–73,
  leakage 52, 53, 60
  piped 45, 46, 47, 72
  price charged for 12, 19, 72
  privatization of 92–93
  right to 19, 72, 92
  role in disease prevention 12, 45, 54
  rural access to 47
  treatment of 42, 90
  urban access to 47, 52, 53
  vendor of 72
waterways 70–71
wetlands 32–33
  dependent species 87
  destruction of 32, 33, 38, 76, 80, 82
  ecological value of 32
women, role in water management 99
World Bank–IMF 93

Yangtze river basin 33, 39, 60, 79
Yemen, water stress 29

Zambezi river basin 43
Zika virus 57